Helping Joe Strong

Other Works by Morris Taylor

Top of the Hill (1987)
Kalimba Song (1997)

Helping Joe Strong

BY MORRIS TAYLOR

Bahá'í Publishing Trust
Wilmette, Illinois

Bahá'í Publishing Trust, Wilmette, IL 60091-2844

00 99 98 97   4 3 2 1

Library of Congress Cataloging-in-Publication Data

Taylor, Morris, 1956–
    Helping Joe Strong / by Morris Taylor.
        p.   cm.
    Includes bibliographical references.
    ISBN 0-87743-266-X
    1. Bahai Faith—History—Fiction.   I. Title.
PS3570.A9464H45   1997
813'.54—dc21   97-29360
                                                       CIP

Table of Contents

Preface

Dear Reader:

This book is not about extraordinary people.

In fact, the people you'll find here are quite ordinary. They're not particularly clever or witty. They don't speak the King's English, their choice of words is not always grammatically correct, and sometimes they're not as tactful as they should be. Instead, this book is about everyday people—people like you and me—who happen to be Bahá'ís. They're Bahá'ís engaged in normal conversations, doing the best they know how to arise and struggle with the same concerns and situations we see in our Bahá'í communities every day.

Keep this in mind when you meet Joe Strong and his friends. They're really a likable bunch if you're willing to look past their all too human frailties!

Another thing I ask you to keep in mind is that this book is not intended to be a set of rules or stringent guidelines. Instead, it should be viewed as a tool, and like any tool it can't be used in every situation. You wouldn't try to saw wood with a hammer, would you? Similarly, it's up to you to determine whether this material could be useful to you and your community in the work you're currently pursuing. What I hope I've provided within these pages is a wealth of thought-provoking and perhaps useful ideas wrapped in a simple story that you can relate to.

So sit back, relax, and share a few hours with Joe Strong—a fine Bahá'í, a dear friend, and one hard-working Assembly member!

—MORRIS TAYLOR
June 1997

Acknowledgments

The core management principles and goal-setting exercises presented within these pages are not original; they are found in countless books and classes devoted to these subjects. I created the various Local Spiritual Assembly checklists and forms, with the exception of the facilitation list, the concept of which was originally introduced to me many years ago by a fellow Assembly member and good friend, Mr. Terrill Hayes.

In addition, I gratefully acknowledge the work of Peter Drucker, Philip Crosby, and Brian Tracy, whose insights on management and personal effectiveness significantly influenced the creation of this book.

Finally, I wish to thank the Bahá'í Publishing Trust of the U.S. for their enthusiasm and support in bringing this project to fruition.

CHAPTER 1

The Phone Call

Joe Strong's arms were full of file boxes and burgeoning accordion folders as he crossed the doorsill. Outside, the driving rain continued unabated. Letting his keys fall to the floor, Joe carefully shifted his weight and tried to close the front door with his free hand, but the humidity from the thunderstorm caused it to stick. Just as he determined to give the door a solidly placed kick, a file began to slip from his arms. As he juggled to catch it, his elbow sharply struck the doorknob and he felt a searing jolt of pain shoot up his arm. He grimaced.

Standing in the foyer of his three-bedroom home, Joe's suit dripped liberally all over the family's new carpeting. For several moments he simply stood in the hallway, soaked with rain, uncertain of what to do next. Finally, he laid the boxes and files of Local Assembly materials against the wall and walked to the downstairs bathroom. He found a clean towel and began to dry his face and hair.

Joe Strong climbed the two steps to the first floor landing and sat down at the kitchen table. He knew he should get out of his wet clothes, but he wasn't in the mood. He fitfully kicked off his shoes and watched them splatter mud on the kitchen floor. It made an awful mess, but his wife and two children were out of town visiting his mother, so there was no one there to chastise him (his wife) or to see his bad example (the kids). He cradled his forehead in his hands and let out a deep and exasperated sigh.

Another Local Spiritual Assembly meeting had ended, and he felt drained. After four hours they had barely worked through a third of the agenda. Years ago, as a new member of the Assembly, he always felt energized and excited after one of their meetings. But things had changed. There were more issues to be addressed, more problems to be remedied, more appeals from every conceivable direction. And then there was the *teaching work* that seemed to him to be nonexistent. Somehow the Assembly never seemed to have enough time to deal with the community's growth and expansion after all the other issues were addressed. It was as if they were inside a cage, running on a large exercise wheel: they were working very hard, going around and around, but there seemed to be very little forward progress.

Joe sat motionless in his wet clothes and tried to analyze his feelings. He wasn't angry, and it wasn't frustration that he felt. No. Tonight the feeling was different. Tonight Joe Strong was scared! Sitting in the Assembly meeting, taking minutes as the recording secretary, he was suddenly struck with the realization that the Assembly seemed stuck. Try as they might, the Assembly members didn't seem to understand what they were doing wrong. And if they couldn't fix "the problem," he feared there was little hope that they would ever accomplish the work that they were divinely mandated to do: *to carry the Message of Bahá'u'lláh to the waiting masses of humanity and thereby transform the world!*

At that moment, a deep, agonizing moan began somewhere in the pit of his stomach. The moan slowly began to rise. Soon it would reach his throat, pass through his lips, and fill the entire kitchen with a woeful sound that would undoubtedly awaken the cat and cause the dog, who was somewhere in the upstairs shadows, to poke his head downstairs and chime in with his own dissonant howl. The two of them together was not a pleasant sound—he knew this because his wife and neighbors had told him so. But he couldn't stop it. The self-indulgent moan of self-pity was coming closer, and closer, and . . .

Then he remembered.

Joe Strong rose from the table and pulled open a drawer in the kitchen counter. He burrowed through scraps of paper and a host of his son's superhero action figures until he found the address book. He hurriedly flipped to the *T*s and ran his finger down the page. "Tu . . . Tuc . . . Tuce . . .Tucker. Wha . . . where's *Tucker*?"

It wasn't there. Suddenly he remembered. He turned the book over and opened the back cover. There, attached to a page yellowed with age and coffee stains, was a small Post-it note. It read, "Julianna Tucker, LSA Bakersfield, 444-2344."

Joe looked at the clock on the kitchen wall. "Twelve-o-five. Is that too late to call?" The moan had stopped about halfway between his stomach and his throat; it was obviously waiting for his decision—but it wouldn't wait long, and Joe thought he heard the dog beginning to stir . . .

Joe dived for the phone. He dialed hurriedly.

The telephone at the other end rang once, twice, three times. Finally a guarded voice answered. "Hello? This is Julianna Tucker."

"Uh . . ." Joe Strong cleared his throat. "Julianna, Ms. Tucker? You may not remember me, but—"

"*Remember* you?" the voice interrupted. "Excuse me, but do you know what time it is?"

Joe Strong stammered an apology. "Well, yes, Ms. Tucker, I know it's late. I apologize, but I'm a Bahá'í and . . ."

"A *Bahá'í*?" the woman on the other end responded, her voice softening noticeably. There was a moment's pause. "You're a Bahá'í? What did you say your name was?"

"Uh, Strong—Joseph Strong. We met at the Community Development Conference last month—in Highburg? You gave a talk on consolidation. I was the guy in the front row with the laptop . . . and the *beeper* that kept going off?"

"Oh yes," said the voice. "I remember you, Mr. Strong—uh, Joe. May I call you Joe?"

"Oh, of course."

"Well, you can call me Julianna, as long as you promise not to call me this late again. Now . . . what can I do for you?"

"It's about my LSA, *our* LSA, here in Somerset. We need help."

"Your LSA? What kind of help?"

"Well, . . . help in functioning. At least I think we need help. Maybe I'm wrong, but somehow I just know we could be more . . . more *efficient*. Bakersfield is just a little larger than our community here in Somerset, and you guys really seem to have it together. I mean people are always talking about what a great community you've got. And the folks who visit here from your area rave about your

Assembly's hard work and how well you do on your goals, and all the great teaching, and—"

"Well, I don't know about all of that," Julianna Tucker interrupted. "People do exaggerate, you know."

"Listen," Joe said. "I know it's awfully late, but . . . could we talk in person? I'd be happy to drive to Bakersfield to meet you."

"Now?"

"Oh," said Joe, remembering the time. "Well, maybe not now, but, say, sometime next week?"

"Well . . . I suppose you could do that if you think it would help. How much time do you think you'll need?"

"I don't know. Whatever you can spare would be great!"

"Hmmm." He could hear Julianna paging through her calendar. "Well . . ." she said finally, "I'm terribly busy next week, but if you don't mind coming down to my office I can spare exactly forty-five minutes between 3:45 and 4:30 P.M. this Thursday. Do you think that will be enough time?"

"Perfect! I'll be there!"

"Okay. My office is in my home—319 Trimbull. It's the corner house with the twin lampposts."

"Got it," said Joe. "Thank you so much!"

"Fine then. I'll see you on Thursday. Don't be late!" *Click!*

Joe hung up the phone and sighed deeply. The water from his wet clothes had formed a puddle under the kitchen table, and his feet were starting to feel cold and numb, but he didn't care.

Joe Strong felt hope.

CHAPTER 2

Joe Strong's Dilemma

Joe sat down in the thick, soft armchair and sipped his cola anxiously.

Julianna Tucker hung up the phone. "Sorry. I really needed to take that call. More ice for your soda?"

"No. This is fine."

"Good." She sat down behind her desk. "'Joe Strong'—that's a nice name for a Bahá'í. '*Strong*,' I mean."

"What? Oh, well I don't feel very strong these days, let me tell you."

"Hmmm." Julianna glanced at her watch. "So, what seems to be the problem? With the Somerset Assembly, that is."

Joe set his cola on a coaster and rubbed his temple. "In Somerset, we need help—big time—in getting our act together. We just aren't getting the job done. We're so . . . so . . . *inefficient*. No matter how hard we work, how many decisions we make, things somehow never seem to turn out the way we intended. It's driving all of us on the Assembly . . . just plain crazy!"

Julianna held up her hand to cut him off. "Hold on, Joe. I'm sure there's something we can do to help. Slow down for a second. Take a deep breath."

Joe took a deep breath.

"Good. Now, Joe, help me out here." She leaned forward across the desk. "Specifically, what *result* are you not getting from *whom*?"

"What result . . . what?" Joe looked at her quizzically. "What do you mean?"

"Well," said Julianna, "you say you need help getting your act together; what *act* are you talking about? You say your Assembly wants to be more efficient; what's your definition of *efficiency*? In other words, it's not quite clear to me what you're looking for, and the fastest way to determine that is for you to say exactly what it is that you want but aren't getting. So I ask again, *specifically*, what result are you not getting . . . and from whom?"

Joe had never thought of the problem in those terms. It took him a moment to collect his thoughts. "Well let's see . . ." he said after a long pause. "Okay," he said. "I'm with you. I'm ready now."

"Good," Julianna said. She reached for a pad and pen. "I'll make a few notes as you talk. I'll just list your concerns one by one."

Joe started to speak. "Well . . . where to begin?" He took another deep breath. "You understand, of course, that this is all from *my* perspective? I mean the Assembly knows I'm talking to you about some of our internal functioning problems. Heck, they even offered to pay for my mileage to come here! But it's not like they told me word for word how to explain things. I could be way out in left field!"

"Purely subjective," Julianna nodded. "I understand."

"Okay, here we go." Joe tapped his fingers together. "Well, first of all . . ."

Julianna's pen started across the blank pad.

"Problem number one: *Our Assembly makes a lot of decisions that it never acts upon.* The way we find out that we've dropped the ball is that weeks or even months later we'll be consulting on something and someone will suddenly say, 'I thought we made a decision about this a long time ago.' The fog starts to lift, but we can't seem to agree on what was decided. So then we search through old minutes for a while, and if no one finds the decision we just give up and start the same discussion all over again!

"Or—and this happens a lot—*we make a decision, but we don't say who's going to carry it out.* Or, if we say who's carrying it out, we don't set a clear deadline, and if we do, we don't honor it. Would you believe, in some cases we've actually had to reverse a good decision solely because we had waited too long to carry it out? We'd lost the window of opportunity."

"Hmmm," said Julianna as she wrote. "I'd call that a lack of follow-through."

Joe nodded in agreement. "Problem number two: instead of one thing after another, it seems like the same thing over and over. For example, *we know we've made a standing policy about a certain subject, but we don't remember the policy!* Or maybe we can't remember the rationale behind the policy, so we're forced to take the time to rethink the whole thing anyway. Then, as we start to reach a decision, someone will say, 'Oh yeah . . . I remember what we said *now!*' Julianna, that drives us nuts!"

"I can imagine. Go on."

"Problem number three: *Committees—we have a number of them, but they don't seem self-sustaining.* We're constantly trying to

strengthen their membership, keep them functioning, but it's a los-
ing battle." Joe, more relaxed now, chuckled to himself. "When I
was a kid I used to see these guys on television—jugglers, I guess.
They would balance these spinning plates on the tops of tall sticks;
then, while this frenetic calliope music played in the background,
the jugglers would run back and forth trying to keep the plates in
motion before they fell to the ground. Well, that's how I feel about
our committees sometimes. As soon as we get one or two of them
up and functioning pretty well, two *others* are starting to topple, and
then . . . *crash*! They're in pieces and we've got to run around patch-
ing them up or start the appointment process all over again!

"Problem number four: *We can't seem to achieve the goals we set
for the community.* At the beginning of each year the Assembly spends
a lot of time setting community goals; we're really very conscientious about studying the messages of the Universal House of Justice
and the National Spiritual Assembly. I'll tell you, the Auxiliary Board
members and other visitors to our community are mighty impressed
when they see our plans. But at the end of the year, when we do an
assessment, we discover that we've hardly made a dent in those goals.
Some Assembly members think that we're always too ambitious—
that we bite off more than we can chew. But I know some of the
goals aren't particularly tough *or* elaborate; I think we're just so busy
doing *other* things that we never get around to doing what we *planned*
to do!" Joe nodded sadly and then looked up. "Uh . . . am I going too
fast?"

"No, no, you're fine. Go on."

"Okay. Let's see. Problem number five: *We're spending an inor-
dinate amount of time dealing with personal problems in the community.*

This person wants a divorce, and that one is having a dispute over a business agreement. This one wants to be reinstated in the Faith; that one is upset because the friends aren't more loving. It takes time to meet with these people, to give them a fair hearing, and a lot *more* time to consult about their problems and reach a decision! By the time we're done, we don't seem to have time for the things that we *say* are important to us but never seem to get to—like teaching!

"And, speaking of teaching, problem number six: *As an Assembly we never talk about teaching—at least not very often or very much.* Our agenda may include a teaching-related issue, but somehow it always seems to get the least amount of time and comes up on the agenda when we're the most tired—if we get to it at all!

"And, speaking of being tired, *it takes us forever to plan events—* I mean things like weddings and proclamations. They just wear us out! And funerals are the worst. I mean with funerals there are so many details to remember, and it's unreasonable to expect the family of the deceased to think of everything—they're already under duress! My guess is that we don't do any of these kinds of events often enough to become good at them! Yep, planning events is a big one! Um . . . I think that was problem number seven."

"Uh-huh."

Joe was on a roll. "You know, our Assembly meets at least once a week and occasionally on weekends, too. In general, I leave the meetings feeling like we worked hard—but I don't know what we did! No—let me change that. I *do* know what we did; I even see what we accomplished. But I'm not sure that what we did had any real *value*—that we're any closer to where we should be as a community. I mean, it's all important, but sometimes I get a sickening feeling that nothing we accomplished at the meeting is going to move the Faith forward. After some of those meetings I'm so exhausted when I get to bed that I'm asleep before I can turn out the lights. And that's not good. After all, I've got a demanding job and a wife and two small kids who need me. And that's the whole point: Time is valuable to me—and to the Faith. I want the work we do on the Assembly to *count* for something—to make a difference. But a lot of the time, I'm just not sure it does!"

Julianna Tucker wrote a few more lines and looked up. "Is that about it?"

Joe grimaced. "That's plenty, wouldn't you say?"

"Okay, then. Let me make sure I understand." She paged through her pad. "You get the minutes done, right?"

"Minutes? Sure. The Assembly insists on them. I crank them out like clockwork."

"Keep agendas—check. Make deliberate plans—check. Your officers must know their jobs and take them seriously, or you wouldn't be doing all the things that you described, and the Assembly members are obviously committed to the work. You have committees and task forces in place; and you're handling personal status cases, so you're clearly concerned about the needs of the individuals in your community. You didn't mention it, but I assume you hold Feasts regularly, and the Assembly doesn't seem to have a problem getting a quorum to meet. Well, Joe, all the essential pieces seem to be in place. It sounds to me as if you've already *got* an efficient LSA!"

"*What?*" Joe was startled by her conclusion. "Well, yes, when you look at it like *that*, but . . . you don't understand!"

"No, I think I do. Your LSA *is* efficient—that is, it's doing all the things Assemblies are supposed to do—but it's not *effective!*"

Joe was puzzled. "What do you mean? Efficient . . . effective—what's the difference?"

Julianna put down her pad and pen. "Efficiency is a tool—*a means to an end,*" she said. "But it's a useless tool if it doesn't help you to achieve your ultimate goals and objectives. Your Assembly sounds like a well-tuned machine that's humming along just fine; you're just not satisfied with your product. In effect, your activity isn't making a connection with your objectives. You're getting results . . . *but not the ones you want!*" Julianna could see that Joe was still perplexed.

"Look at it this way," she explained. "In my work as a consultant, I meet business people every day who are quite *efficient* in what they do . . . but they do all the wrong things. They make poor choices in goal setting and prioritization, and as a result they fail to make significant progress. For all their efficiency, they aren't getting anywhere! On the other hand, sometimes I find executives who are extremely *effective*—leaders in their field! But for them, effectiveness has become a hit-or-miss process. They succeed only through sheer determination. If they would learn to be more efficient in using their time, money, and human resources, their success would become regular and systematic rather than sporadic. Get the picture?"

"Yes . . . I think I see now." Joe was quiet for a moment. "That's it," he said thoughtfully. "We *are* efficient. But for all our work, we don't seem to have any tangible progress to show for it. That's definitely our problem! So can you help us?"

"Maybe. But first I have to ask you: Is this a one-man crusade? Are you alone with these concerns, or does the entire Assembly feel the way you do?"

"Oh we've definitely consulted about it—a lot! And they know I've come to talk with you about the way your Assembly does things here in Bakersfield—like I said, you've got quite a reputation. There's unquestionably a consensus that things could be a lot better. I mean none of us are happy with the way things have been going. But I also don't think any of us want you to come in and lecture us—no offense."

"Don't worry, I don't think that's the answer either. But maybe I can show you a couple of things our Assembly does—a few tools and techniques we've adopted to increase *our* effectiveness. Do you think that would help?"

"That's why I came. I'm open to any ideas you may have."

"Alright then. I'll make a deal with you."

"A deal?" said Joe.

"Right. First of all, the most critical factor in improving personal effectiveness is attitude. Without really *wanting* to improve, without an honest effort, little progress will be made. Your Assembly needs to ask itself if it really wants to change and is willing to make the effort to improve its effectiveness."

"Believe me," said Joe with conviction, "we're ready to do things differently!"

"Good. Second, I know these ideas work for us, but they may not be suited to your Assembly's needs or to your community's present stage of development. If your Assembly likes a particular idea, use it. If they don't like it, or if there's serious disagreement about it, don't use it. Agreed?"

"Agreed. No forcing!"

"Great," Julianna stood up from her desk. "Listen, Joe, I'm glad we could share this time together, but now you really must go."

"Go? But what's next? What do we do?"

Julianna scribbled a name and telephone number on the top sheet of her pad and gave it to Joe. "His name is Farhad—he's our general secretary. Give him a call in few days. I'll tell him to expect to hear from you."

"But what am I supposed to say to him?"

"He's the perfect person to talk to about managing meetings. I think that's the perfect place for you to start your journey towards increased effectiveness."

Joe took the paper. "Oh. Well, alright." He folded the paper and put it in his shirt pocket.

They walked out of the office and down the hall. She patted him on the back. "Forty-five minutes is really all I could spare today. I'm sure you understand."

"Yes, of course. I really appreciate your time."

"Happy to help." Julianna Tucker pumped his hand in a firm handshake. "Good-bye!"

Joe heard a door slam. Stunned, he suddenly realized that he was standing on the stoop outside the house.

She had walked him out the front door without his even realizing it!

Joe got in his car. He felt dazed and a little agitated; after all, this wasn't what he had expected. He sat quietly for a moment, then reached for the pad and pen that he always kept in the car's glove compartment. He paused in thought, pen poised in hand, then wrote on the top sheet of the pad:

There's a difference between _efficiency_ and _effectiveness._

Being efficient saves time, energy, and other resources. But efficiency is useless if you're not getting the results you want.

In order to get results, you have to be _effective!_

"Hmmm," Joe thought. "This should be interesting."

CHAPTER 3

Managing Meetings

L et me guess. She asked you, 'What *results* are you not getting from *whom*?' Am I right?"

"Sounds like you know her pretty well," said Joe as he eased back on the couch. It was the week following his meeting with Julianna Tucker, and Joe sat comfortably in the home of Farhad Soheili, the general secretary of the Local Spiritual Assembly of Bakersfield.

Farhad smiled warmly. "That J.T.'s something, isn't she? No nonsense—she goes straight to the heart of the matter. She makes a pretty good chairperson! Here, have some more tea. It's a special Persian blend. My brother-in-law imports it from overseas."

Joe held his cup out as Farhad poured the tea. "So, you're married?"

"Oh, yes. My wife and I have been married for five years. We have two little girls."

"How do you find the time to be general secretary? Isn't it a lot of work for a community your size?"

"Oh, yes," said Farhad, amiably nodding. "But you make the time for Bahá'u'lláh," he smiled. "And I get a lot of help from the other members of the Assembly. We work together." Farhad put the tea on the end table. "So, why did J.T. send you to see me? From what you've said of your conversation with her, I would think she'd be able to tell you quite a bit about some of the ideas we've adopted to help our Assembly."

"Well," said Joe, "actually, she said you were the best person to talk to about managing meetings. She seemed to think that would be a good place for our Assembly to begin practicing some of that effectiveness she was talking about." Joe flipped open the small notepad he had brought from the glove compartment of his car. "So, what makes your meetings . . . *effective?*"

"Well, you know," said Farhad, "we have a lot of lovers of Bahá'u'lláh on our Assembly; really, they will do anything for the Cause. But they are also very smart people, very educated. So we are not afraid to try different kinds of things to solve our problems. Sometimes one of our members will read something—maybe in a book or a magazine article on management or organizational design—and that person might suggest that we modify the basic idea to fit our needs. As long as it doesn't compromise Bahá'í principles and it's effective, we will try it."

"That's an interesting perspective," said Joe. "But I find that a lot of Bahá'ís assume that everything we need is already in the Bahá'í writings somewhere—that there's no need to look for ideas outside the teachings."

"Oh yes, everything we need to *guide* us is there, but maybe not every little detail for every situation. This is why God gave us a brain.

For example, there is nothing in the writings to tell a carpenter how to build a house. Does this mean that we should not live in houses? There is also nothing to tell a doctor how to remove a diseased organ from a person's body. But Bahá'u'lláh gave us principles and ethical standards that can be applied to virtually everything we do. In this instance, the principles influence the decisions and behavior of the craftsman who is engaged in commerce and business, as well as the doctor who must turn to God for guidance and divine assistance. So I think the writings are like a scale upon which we can weigh the relative value and worth of different ideas, proposals, and suggestions. If we are unbiased and consider all these things in the light of God's standards and principles, I believe we will know which things are good and helpful and which ones are not."

Joe nodded thoughtfully. "That makes sense." He wrote a few words in his notepad.

"Now, before I go any further," said Farhad, "you do understand that this is just the way *we* do things. It doesn't mean it's the right way or even the best way. It's just the way that works for us right now."

Joe remembered hearing similar words from the chair of the Bakersfield Assembly. "Oh yes, I understand."

"Okay. Well, you are interested in what makes an effective meeting. First of all, I can tell you that effective meetings are as much the result of what happens *between* the meetings as they are what happens *during* the meetings."

"You mean planning."

"Yes, planning is a part of it," said Farhad, "but there is more involved. Meetings of any kind are, in general, very expensive in terms of resources—time, money, physical and emotional energy, lost opportunities to be with your family and to work on personal projects, and so on. So the last thing you want to do is bring nine people together without a clear purpose and a clearly defined expected outcome. I know from my professional work that a lot of meetings are insufficiently prepared and organized, poorly managed, or inadequately evaluated. Most of them take too long and don't leave the participants with a feeling that progress has been made. When our Assembly sits down as a body, there is no doubt that certain issues have already been addressed in preparation for the meeting and that the time spent will be productive and very fruitful. I guess I would call those issues *meeting basics*. Let me share them with you."

As Farhad spoke, Joe Strong wrote the following in his notepad.

Four Issues to Address
When Planning an Assembly Meeting

1. Is this meeting necessary? When the Assembly meets, there should be a *need* to exchange information; a *reason* to share ideas, pool resources and opinions; and a specific objective in analyzing difficult problems and bringing consultation to bear in making decisions in complex situations. If there is no pressing reason to meet, if the work of the community and the institution will go forward effectively without the Assembly's coming together, then don't meet. This principle must be balanced with the fact that there is probably a great deal more the Assembly could be doing to advance the Cause if the members were to meditate about it and set their hearts and minds to the task. One way to examine the question of whether a meeting is necessary is to ask, "If the Assembly did not meet until (a future date), what would remain undone, and what opportunities would be lost?"

2. Is the entire Assembly needed? Could the immediate work be handled by a smaller task force or subcommittee of the Assembly that could review the issue(s) at hand and prepare a proposal to be reviewed later by the full Assembly? Things such as the coordination of the community calendar and the scheduling of events, planning for the Nineteen Day Feast or holy day observances, and the updating of community records and statistics can be addressed initially by a few Assembly members assigned to the task, perhaps on a rotating basis.

3. Choosing a suitable time. Whenever possible, all nine members should be available to attend the meeting. Pick a starting time when people can be present and ready to begin. The members should also have time to prepare for the meeting properly—completing their individual assignments, reading minutes and proposals in advance, etc. For the sake of individual schedule planning, the Assembly may find it advantageous to hold its meetings at the same time on a regular basis, such as *the first Sunday morning of each Bahá'í month,* or *every Monday at 7:30 P.M.,* or *the first and third Wednesday of every Gregorian month*. In any case, be sure everyone knows about the meeting, including the time and location. Give good advance notice and, whenever possible, verify the *next* meeting date at the end of each meeting.

4. Set up the room properly. The room should be large enough to accommodate the nine members comfortably. You may also wish to consider a location that will easily accommodate guests from time to time. The room should be neat and orderly, and reference materials such as copies of the writings of Bahá'-u'lláh and 'Abdu'l-Bahá and letters of the Guardian and the Universal House of Justice should be accessible. When possible, it is also helpful if all the Assembly members and any guests can gather at a single table. The table should be large enough to provide adequate space for all participants to lay out their individual materials and to take notes if desired.

Joe turned to a fresh page in his notepad as Farhad continued . . .

Nine Points to Remember *during* an Assembly Meeting

1. Start on time—as soon as you have a quorum. If you wait for tardy participants, you will always start late. People will respect the institution's time if it respects theirs. Starting on time displays professionalism and a sense of order and control.

2. Start the meeting in the proper attitude of prayer and reverence. Always begin with prayers for guidance and assistance. It may be helpful to start the meetings with a mini-deepening or by sharing a few brief quotations to inspire your deliberations. The purpose should be to remind each member as to why he or she is there, and to put their full trust and confidence in Bahá'u'lláh.

3. Try to recognize critical points and occurrences during the meeting. This is largely the responsibility of the chairperson, but all members should feel accountable. It is important that an atmosphere of loving congeniality and good humor permeate the meetings. However, it is wise to diplomatically call attention to distracting conversations, digressions, and differences of opinion that have become exclusive dialogues between a small number of individuals. Learn to recognize when an impasse has been reached, and be sensitive to conditions that may lead to hasty or wrong decisions.

4. Make sure goals are being achieved. The best way is for the chairperson to state clearly at the beginning of each new topic the objective of the consultation. Is this an "FYI-only" discussion? Is the objective to identify an individual or group of individuals to serve on a committee? Is the Assembly to select a location, write a mandate, respond to a specific request, etc.? In this way, if the Assembly gets bogged down in its deliberations, it can refer back to its previously identified objective to get back on track.

5. Clearly restate all decisions. Once a decision appears to have been reached, the chairperson should restate it for clarification, and the recording secretary should read it back to ensure that the Assembly's intention is accurately captured. After an issue is discussed, the results should be summarized and should include *what* has to be done, by *whom*, and by *when*.

6. Allow for a mix of social, spiritual, and business activities. Meetings that are all business often drain the energy of the participants. Concentration and interest begin to wane. The meeting is more likely to remain focused and achieve its objectives if all three needs—spiritual, social, and business—are planned for and addressed.

Plan the meeting so that the first ten to fifteen minutes are devoted exclusively to chatting and socializing. The Assembly members should use the time to inquire about each other's personal news, accomplishments, and current concerns. Don't let this period be used as a margin for lateness; build it into your agenda. This technique fills an important need and also reduces the likelihood that chatter will interfere with the "business" part of the meeting later.

It is also important to reenergize participants from time to time. Here are two methods that can easily be incorporated into most meetings:

a. Take a *spiritual break*. Take two to three minutes for spiritual meditation and inner reflection. Sometimes dramatic changes occur after a break of this nature.

b. Take a *social break*. Encourage the members to stand up, stretch, and—most important—converse with each

other on non-Assembly related matters. This kind of activity almost always breathes new life into the work of the
group.

**7. Set a specific time to end the meeting, and close the meet-
ing on time whenever possible.** Individuals will tend to remain more alert and focused during the meeting if they know
that it will end at a definite time. This kind of deadline will
also help keep the consultation on track and generally moving
forward. If you run over the allotted time, finish only what *must*
be done and then list the remainder under *unfinished business* to
be given priority attention at the next meeting. A commitment
to handle unfinished business in this manner ensures that you
won't fall too far behind and that older items won't be subse-
quently deleted from the agenda because they weren't handled
in a timely manner.

8. Prepare minutes that clearly summarize the meeting. They
should be produced and distributed as soon as possible—within
twenty-four to forty-eight hours is ideal. One of the worst mistakes to make after a meeting is having *no* minutes; the second
worst is having *bad* minutes.

Farhad shared with Joe a simple format for Assembly minutes. (See
Illus. 3.1.)

Minutes of the Spiritual Assembly
of the Bahá'ís of Bakersfield

Meeting date:
Location:
Attending:
Absent:
Start: _____ A.M./P.M.   End: _____ A.M./P.M.
1. Subject:
Important points:
Decision:

2. Subject:
Important points:
Decision:

3. Subject:
Important points:
Decision:

4. Subject:
Important points:
Decision:

Items tabled:

Submitted by: _____

Illustration 3.1. A simple format for minutes

9. From time to time, examine the course and outcome of your meetings. Are the goals and objectives of your meetings understood by all of the Assembly members? Does everyone receive the agenda? Do the meetings start on time? Does everyone keep to the agenda? Do you achieve the goals of your meetings? Are tasks assigned and deadlines set? In terms of the entire meeting, how much time is spent inefficiently and/or ineffectively? A periodic assessment of this nature will help the Assembly to identify potential weaknesses before they become debilitating problems.

Joe Strong put down his pen. "That's a lot to think about."

Farhad smiled. "It all makes a difference."

"May I ask you about your consultation?" Joe asked rather sheepishly.

"But of course. We're no experts at it, but I can tell you our understanding of it and how we try to make it work."

"Well," said Joe, "we seem to lose a lot of time trying to reach consensus. My understanding is that consensus is a good thing, but, gosh, sometimes it seems like we go around and around for the longest time. What's the secret?"

"I don't think there is a secret; I think it just takes a lot of hard work. But why don't you tell me just a little bit about how *your* Assembly consults?"

"Well," Joe began, "there's nothing unusual there. We pretty much follow the approach suggested in a lot of Bahá'í books. What we generally do, in sequence, is:

1. Define the issue being discussed.

2. Ascertain all the pertinent facts.

3. Identify the spiritual and administrative principles pertinent to the issue.

4. Apply the spiritual and administrative principles to the issue in a full, frank, and loving discussion, giving everyone the opportunity to express their opinion.

5. Adopt a resolution by consensus or, if necessary, by a majority vote; and

6. If the decision requires action, decide how the action will be carried out."

"Sounds good to me," said Farhad.

"Yeah, but the *consensus* part . . . that can be pretty difficult sometimes."

"Ah, yes." Farhad stood up from his chair and paced a little. "Let's think about this. A consensus is basically a general agreement among the members that allows everyone to support a decision. When we want a consensus, which is pretty much all of the time, we have two rules: don't vote, and don't expect complete agreement."

"Wait a minute," said Joe. "I can understand the 'don't vote' rule. We've learned the hard way that voting tends to cut off consultation too quickly. But 'don't expect complete agreement'? I thought that was the point of consensus."

"Yes, in a sense it is. But don't forget: we're trying to reach a decision everyone can support. That doesn't necessarily mean that everyone on the Assembly agrees that the decision is absolutely the best one. It means that everyone on the Assembly feels that his or her concerns have been heard and adequately addressed. When a direction is chosen, the desired *details* may vary from person to person, but generally each member is comfortable with the decision."

Joe nodded. "I see what you mean now. But that still leaves the question of how you reach that point."

"Well, now that you've asked me, I remember that J. T. does do something very interesting—and very effective.

"Whenever we're about to make a decision, *first*, she restates the proposed decision for clarity. *Second*, she asks if anyone *disagrees*. If the feeling is not unanimous, she always asks the individuals who are not in agreement one or more of the following questions:

1. *What information do you need so you can support this decision?*
2. *What results of this decision do you think we have neglected to consider?*
3. *How can we build on this idea so we can reach a decision you can support?"*

"Hey," said Joe, his hand moving feverishly across his notepad, "those are good questions. I can think of a couple of situations right now that would have been resolved a lot quicker if we had used that approach!"

"It's effective, alright." At that moment, two small girls with long dark hair raced into the room. One jumped directly into the lap of Joe's host; the other waved two balloons in his face, smiling broadly.

"Oh!" said Farhad, "look who is home! Did you go to the birthday party?"

"*Yessss!*" they giggled.

Farhad drew them both close and hugged them. "Say hello to Papa's friend. This is Mr. Strong." He gestured towards Joe. "He is a Bahá'í, just like us. This is Sahba and Mehrik."

"It's a pleasure to meet you," said Joe. The two small girls smiled shyly.

"Where's Mommy? Is she in the kitchen?"

The two girls nodded.

"Alright. Go to the kitchen. I have to finish my meeting with Mr. Strong."

The two girls left obediently.

"They're very cute," said Joe.

"Thank you. This is the time of day when they usually practice their Hidden Words with me while their mother is making dinner."

"Oh, I'm sorry," Joe apologized as he rose from the coach. "I should leave."

"No, no. Sit. We have time. Besides, we haven't talked about agendas yet. Let me get something for you." Farhad disappeared for a brief moment then returned with two sheets of paper. "You can have this if you like. This is a blank outline of our Assembly's agenda format."

Joe looked at the outline. (See Illus. 3.2, page 30.)

Farhad went on to explain the agenda outline. "The Assembly chairperson and general secretary are responsible for preparing our agenda. We meet in advance to review the incoming correspondence, any unfinished business from the previous meeting, and to consider any input we may have received between meetings from other Assembly members. When the members arrive for the actual meeting, there are copies of the agenda for everyone.

"We only put on the agenda those items which we plan to address at that meeting. Beside each of these items we place an *estimated time* (noted as 'est. time' on the agenda), which signifies how much time the chairperson and secretary feel will be required to

Spiritual Assembly of the Bahá'ís of Bakersfield

Date: _____

I. *Opening* (45 minutes) Start Time: _____
        Social time
        LSA Prayer
        LSA deepening
        Review minutes, agenda
        General Secretary's report

II. *Plan Status* - est. time: _____

III. *Expansion/Proclamation* - est. time: _____
        1.
        2.

IV. *Consolidation* - est. time: _____
        1.
        2.

V. *Personal Affairs* - est. time: _____
        1.
        2.

VI. *Administrative Issues* - est. time: _____
        1.
        2.

VII. *Closing* - Start time: _____
        1. Next meeting: _____
        2. Community prayers

Illustration 3.2. An agenda outline

Spiritual Assembly of the Bahá'ís of Bakersfield

Correspondence for meeting of: _____

Incoming items (including date and action taken)
>   1.
>   2.
>   3.
>   4.
>   5.

Outgoing items (including date)
>   1.
>   2.
>   3.
>   4.
>   5.

Future agenda items
(including date item was added to agenda)

Expansion/Proclamation
>   1.
>   2.

Consolidation
>   1.
>   2.

Personal Affairs
>   1.
>   2.

Administrative
>   1.
>   2.

address that particular topic. The Assembly shoots for these times, and, although we aren't always successful, it gives us more focus and a much better chance of completing the entire meeting's agenda.

"We have a number of broad categories, as you can see:

Opening: This includes prayers and deepening, a social period, and a review of the agenda as well as the last set of minutes.

Plan Status: Here we discuss the status of the goals and objectives of our current teaching plan. This is a brief but important overview that enables us to make any necessary adjustments in terms of priorities, allocation of resources, and so on.

Expansion/Proclamation: This includes all events, activities, and efforts related to the teaching work.

Consolidation: This is where we consult on activities and concerns in terms of strengthening the community, promoting unity, and deepening the believers.

Personal Affairs: This involves issues concerning the status of individuals such as weddings, personal problems, possible deprivation of administrative rights, and the like.

Administrative: This includes the secretary's full report, the treasurer's report, and any matter that doesn't fall directly into the expansion or consolidation categories.

"One thing I should point out is that we date all items on the agenda. The date should indicate when the item first came to the Assembly's attention. On our agenda, any piece of business older than three weeks automatically becomes a priority on the next agenda.

On the back of the agenda we list *incoming correspondence* and *outgoing correspondence.* This area shows all the correspondence that has come in since the last meeting so that the Assembly as a body is aware, and any individual member can call to our attention any items of significance that may require additional attention.

Future agenda items: Here we keep track of items that require the Assembly's attention but won't be addressed at the current meeting. We also note the date each item was initially presented to the Assembly so that we don't let it sit on the future list too long without being handled. Listing things in this way makes the entire Assembly aware and also gives individuals a chance to suggest a change in priorities if appropriate.

"We also review the agenda at the start of the meeting, immediately after our prayers and deepening. The chair or secretary usually gives a brief report at this point so that the members know exactly what's in front of them and can discuss any agenda changes they think are needed.

"As we go through the agenda, we do it with the idea in mind that we will handle each item only once. That is, we try to make a decision on each item the first time we discuss it unless further research or information gathering is required. In that case, we determine to handle it only twice. In either situation, each item will be handled in one of four ways. It will either be:

1. *Tossed,*
2. *Referred or delegated to others,*

3. *Acted upon by the Assembly itself,* or

4. *Filed for future reference.*

"In many cases, the Assembly has given me, as general secretary, the authority to make decisions of this nature in advance of the meeting. If I can come prepared to report this information in my secretary's report, or if it is noted in one of the correspondence lists, the meeting goes faster and the LSA is still informed, but, if necessary, any action I have taken can still be corrected or changed as the Assembly deems appropriate.

"A good agenda can make a big difference," Farhad concluded. "When the recording secretary prepares the minutes, he simply follows the outline of the agenda, noting any essential facts or considerations that came out during the consultation, the specific decisions made, and any items tabled. Once he adds the notes on attendance and the starting and ending times, his work is done."

"This is amazing," said Joe. "I wish we had been using some of these ideas earlier. I can see some really significant time-savers here. Tell me, with so many good ideas about preparing for the meeting and mapping out an effective agenda, what's usually your biggest problem?"

"That's easy," Farhad nodded. "By far, the biggest problem is realistically estimating how much time to give each subject. Remember, Joe: everything takes longer than expected."

Joe nodded. "Yes. I'll remember that." Joe flipped his notepad shut. "You can't imagine how much I appreciate this, Farhad. I'm going to ask my Assembly to consider some of these ideas right away. But I've taken too much of your time already. I really should be going."

"What? And miss dinner? You can't leave without eating with us."

"Well, I don't know . . ."

"If you don't have dinner, you will be insulting my wife, and my little girls will cry. You must honor my Persian hospitality!" Farhad gestured toward the kitchen.

Joe swallowed his objections . . . and a lot of *tahdig*.

CHAPTER 4

Forward Progress

Joe Strong took his notepad to the next meeting of the Somerset Assembly. He told them what he had learned about efficiency and effectiveness. He told them about the ideas for managing meetings. And . . .

The Assembly liked what it heard.

The Somerset Assembly began to implement the ideas with great success, which made Joe and all the other members feel much better about their work.

A few weeks later Joe called Farhad on the phone. They talked about the Assembly's progress, and Farhad offered his congratulations on the Assembly's commitment to try to be more effective.

"You know," said Joe, "our meetings really are better now. And this agenda format really does help us to focus our efforts. But now we realize just how much there is to do. I mean, our agendas are so full, we're having a difficult time selecting our top priorities."

"Hmmm," said Farhad. "If I understand you correctly, you want to know how we go about determining what our goals should be."

"You've got it exactly. So what do you do? Spin a dial, or maybe flip a coin?"

Farhad laughed. "Not exactly. But, believe it or not, J.T. called me just a few days after you and I met. She said this would probably be your next question. That J.T.—she's really something else, isn't she?"

"Yes, I'd say so," replied Joe, a little agitated.

"She asked me," Farhad continued, "to give you the name and phone number of our treasurer, Mr. Frank Lane. He's a strategic planning specialist by profession and also happens to be a real whiz at analyzing the plans from the senior institutions of the Faith and helping us to translate them into viable goals and objectives for the local community. He's a pretty busy guy, but I'm sure he'll make time to talk to you—especially if you bribe him with some Ben and Jerry's Cherry Garcia ice-cream! That's his favorite!"

"Cherry Garcia . . . got it. Thanks for the tip!"

"You bet. If you have a pencil, I'll give you his number right now."

CHAPTER 5

Setting Goals and Priorities

My son just graduated from law school; he's applying for jobs in Manhattan. My daughter's in college now, although it's all her mother and I can do to keep her there. She met a Korean fella at a young Bahá'í professionals conference in Mississippi, got engaged, and now they're determined to pioneer to Africa as soon as they get married and finish their degrees. Says she's going to teach elementary school in one of the South African homelands. *Imagine:* a young African-American woman with a Korean husband." Frank Lane nodded with a wry smile. "This is truly a new day, Joe. Please, please have a seat."

The two men sat down on the enclosed sundeck. Frank was tall and broad and built like a football lineman. He was in his fifties with salt-and-pepper hair and a jovial face that belied his serious nature. "Are you sure you won't have some Cherry Garcia?" he asked. "It's just me and my wife at home now, and *we* don't need all of that."

"Oh, I'm sure," said Joe. "My wife's got me on a strict dessert diet of nothing but frozen yogurt!"

"Oh, believe me, I understand. Yeah—that Farhad's a funny guy. He knows Cherry Garcia's my weakness!" Frank sat back on the couch. "So, Joseph Strong, your Assembly wants to be more effective in selecting goals and setting priorities?"

"That's right. It seems like the more we consult, the more we realize there is to do. Of course we want to do everything at once—the Faith has so many needs. But we know if we take that approach, we run the risk of not doing *anything* very well!"

"Sounds like a familiar problem," said Frank. "You see, Joe, I work as a strategic planning specialist, and I'll be the first to admit that my professional interest has carried over to my work on the Assembly. I *believe* in goal-setting—both short-term and long-term. Maybe I can make a few suggestions that will at least get your Assembly started."

"Great," said Joe. "Now I know this is very basic, but every few years our Assembly wrestles with the idea that maybe we shouldn't set any goals at all. Maybe we should just work on improving the processes in the community and the goals will take care of themselves."

"Hmmm. That obviously raises a very good question: Why set goals at all? Over the years, I've been on a few Assemblies that proceeded in just the manner you describe. I suppose there's an argument to be made for it. But let me share something with you. I once heard an analogy that went like this:

"Working without goals is like bowling with a curtain blocking your view of the pins. You roll the ball, and it disappears behind the curtain. You hear noise and you *think* maybe a pin or two fell, but you aren't sure because you can't see what's happening. How long do you think bowling would remain popular if it were played that way? Not very long, I'll tell you. In order to stay motivated and ultimately become successful, people need something to *aim* at, and they need to see the *results* of their efforts. That's where goal-setting comes in. Goals are like the bowling pins that people aim to hit. And when they successfully knock down a few, they're encouraged and motivated to try even harder."

"That's a great analogy," chuckled Joe.

"Uh-huh! Now, once you understand the importance of goals, the question becomes, 'How do I decide what goals to set?'"

Joe Strong opened his notepad and began to write.

"Like I said, I've been serving on Local Assemblies for quite a few years," Frank continued. "Not long ago I began to ask myself why organizations, including Assemblies, make certain decisions. I've noticed some patterns that might sound familiar to you.

"The decisions are usually based on one of the following reasons:

Habit. We've always done things a certain way. Our choices are so automatic that it never occurs to us that there may be a need to change or improve.

The demands of others. We allow other people's priorities to overshadow our own.

Avoidance. To escape doing things that may be difficult or unpleasant, we choose activities that keep us busy but not very productive.

Short-term gratification. In the absence of a long-range vision or plan, we impulsively pursue whatever activity seems enjoyable or reasonable at the moment.

Default. We wait for a worthwhile goal, idea, or project to "appear" from the outside, and while waiting we do things that are relatively inconsequential.

Conscious decision. We carefully outline our goals and objectives and systematically pursue them.

"Which of these do you think your LSA relates to the most, Joe?"

"Gosh. I'd have to say it's probably a tie between habit and the demands of others. I guess that's not good, huh?"

"Oh, I'm not saying that there's anything *wrong* with making decisions based on the demands of others, or out of habit, or by default, or for any of the other reasons—*unless* you're not happy with the results you're getting." Frank Lane pointed an emphatic finger in Joe's direction. "If you're not happy with the results, you have to stop, evaluate the situation, and begin making more choices based on conscious decisions!

"The big question for a Local Spiritual Assembly is, *What do we really want for our community?*

"What is the Assembly's hope for the community over the next twenty years? What would it like to see the community accomplish within the next *five* years? If your Assembly were to learn that the community's freedom to grow and develop would be abruptly cut off *six months* from today, how would it spend the remaining time?

"Of course, in some ways these are rhetorical questions; they do make you stop and think. The basic resource we all start with is time—the minutes, hours, days, and years ahead of us. Answering questions such as these helped our Assembly to discover what it really wanted to do, helped motivate us to do it, and gave greater meaning to the way we spent our time. Having goals and clearly defined priorities gave us direction and removed a lot of self-doubt about whether what we were doing had value. And it provided us with a measuring stick for determining the relative worth of alternate activities as they came along."

"So you really did address each of these questions?" probed Joe.

"Yes, we really did. And the result was a set of goals that . . . well, surprised us a bit. Then, once we had clearly defined goals and priorities, *we wrote them down* and kept them close at hand."

"You emphasize the action of writing them down. Why is that?"

"That's easy," Frank replied. "Writing requires you to be more specific. You have to narrow down your aims because you can only write a limited number of words compared to all the hundreds of thousands you've exchanged and considered during consultation. And, like I said, our selection of what to write down indicated priorities that surprised us."

"You know, I think we might like to give that a try," offered Joe. "Tell me again exactly how you went about this exercise."

"Well, here's what you do, Joe."

Joe wrote down the following:

An Exercise in Goal-Setting

1. Take a copy of the current teaching plan of the Universal House of Justice and the companion plan from the National Spiritual Assembly. Study these carefully, identifying the salient categories and areas in need of focused attention. Your list of major areas might look like this:

Marriage and Family Life

Spiritual Development of Individuals

Expansion/Enrollments

Development of Feasts and Holy Days

The Bahá'í Funds

Education of Children

Completion of the Arc

Community Deepening and Consolidation

External Affairs/Public Relations

Development of the Local Spiritual Assembly

Education on the Ḥuqúqu'lláh

2. Next, take three to five minutes to list as many goals for your community as you can think of in each category. If you do this as an Assembly, have someone act as scribe while the Assembly brainstorms aloud, taking one category at a time. Work from the assumption that you have an extended period of time in which to accomplish these goals, approximately twenty years.

3. Next, take three to five minutes to brainstorm on the question, "What would you like to see the community accomplish in the next five years?"

4. Now take three to five minutes to brainstorm on the question, "If you knew that your community's freedom to grow and develop would be abruptly cut off six months from today, how would you use your time and resources until then?"

5. Now spend an additional five minutes reviewing and improving your goal statements in answering all three questions.

"As you review all three sets of answers," Frank explained, "you may find that the goals you have set in response to step three were a natural extension of those you identified in step two; this is good. Some Assemblies also find that the goals generated in step four (the six-months question) is a continuation of the previous two, but other Assemblies find that their perspectives change radically when they imagine that their time is limited (i.e., six months). The six-months question will help identify some things you would do if forced by circumstances to be more focused and objective about your community's progress. The point is, with proper prioritization, there's no real reason not to start doing the things you feel are most important immediately.

The Challenge of Setting Priorities

"Now you have a potential list of goals, but, if you're like most Assemblies, you've thought of more to do than there is time to do it. You have to face the challenge of deciding what's most important and setting priorities. Some choices will probably be easy; others more difficult. But don't worry; you can always come back and make adjustments later if necessary.

How to Set Priorities

"Here's one way to decide where to focus your energy and other resources during a given period of time."

1. Review your twenty-year list, and spend a few minutes selecting your *top three* goals from the entire list.
2. Do the same for your five-years list and your six-months list.

3. At this point you have a total of nine goals selected from the three lists. List them on a flip chart so everyone can see them. For example, your list might look like this:

    • Improve the overall quality of the Nineteen-Day Feast.
    • Sponsor a series of deepenings on Bahá'í marriage and family life.
    • Increase adult Bahá'í membership by 20 percent in the next twelve months.
    • Start Bahá'í children's classes for ages 5–14.
    • Purchase a new computer for the Assembly.
    • Buy a local Bahá'í center.
    • Increase youth participation in all community activities.
    • Have three large-scale proclamations during the coming year.
    • Increase fund participation by 15 percent.

4. Next, choose between each of the nine items as follows, and on your list put a check mark beside your choice. In making your choices you will want to consider the guidance of the senior institutions, the needs of your specific community (both Bahá'í and non-Bahá'í), any groundwork that has already been laid, and so on. Make your choice(s) by answering the following questions:

    What is more important—item 1 or item 2? (Put a check mark beside your choice.)
    Now choose the most important item in each of the following

pairs, placing a check mark beside your choice: 1 or 3, 1 or 4, 1 or 5, 1 or 6, 1 or 7, 1 or 8, *and* 1 or 9.

Continue choosing between pairs of items as follows:

2 or 3, 2 or 4, 2 or 5, 2 or 6, 2 or 7, 2 or 8, 2 or 9.

3 or 4, 3 or 5, 3 or 6, 3 or 7, 3 or 8, 3 or 9.

4 or 5, 4 or 6, 4 or 7, 4 or 8, 4 or 9.

5 or 6, 5 or 7, 5 or 8, 5 or 9.

6 or 7, 6 or 8, 6 or 9.

7 or 8, 7 or 9.

8 or 9.

When you are done, your list will look similar to this:

- Improve the overall quality of the   ✓✓✓✓
  Nineteen-Day Feast.
- Sponsor a series of deepenings   ✓✓✓
  on Bahá'í marriage and family life.
- Increase adult Bahá'í membership by   ✓✓✓✓✓
  20 percent in the next twelve months.
- Start Bahá'í children's classes for ages 5–14.   ✓✓✓
- Purchase a new computer for the Assembly.   ✓✓
- Buy a local Bahá'í center.   ✓
- Increase youth participation   ✓✓✓✓
  in all community activities.
- Have three large-scale proclamations   ✓✓✓✓✓✓
  during the coming year.
- Increase fund participation by 15 percent.   ✓✓✓

The item that has the most check marks is currently of

the greatest importance to your Local Assembly, and your time and other resources should be allocated so that you can begin work on this goal immediately. The item with the second highest number of checks is the second most important, and so on through your list.

Planning

"This is so simple," said Joe, pausing with pen in hand. "And yet, it really does tell you what's important to you."

"It sure does," Frank nodded.

"So, now that we have our major goals, we have to make plans to achieve them. What's an easy way to go about that?"

Frank held up both hands. "Whoa, Joe! That's not a simple question! I do this for a living, you know. I conduct a week-long workshop on that very question and charge high-powered executives thousands of dollars. But . . ." he grinned warmly, "maybe I can boil it down to a few basics."

Joe was all ears.

"First," Frank began, "if you always plan your work before you begin, you'll yield tremendous results in productivity and performance. It's been estimated that one minute in planning saves you five minutes in execution. In other words, your investment in planning gets you a 500 percent return. Where else can you get a 500 percent return on your investment?

"Now, one very simple but effective tool for planning is something called a *work flow sequence*."

"A work flow sequence?" Joe queried.

Frank took out a sheet of paper and began drawing several boxes on it. "Look here. Any task the Assembly undertakes is made up of a series of smaller tasks which, when accomplished sequentially, produce a final product or service for the community.

"For example, an Assembly may wish to prepare an annual report. That task would involve several smaller tasks such as gathering data, identifying the major themes and achievements of the year, creating an outline for the report, preparing a rough draft, reviewing and revising the draft, and eventually approving the final report.

"This series of tasks can be illustrated using a work flow sequence, like this." (See Illus. 5.1.)

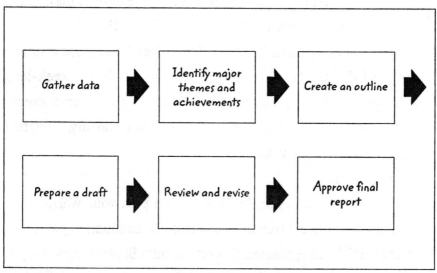

Illustration 5.1. A work flow sequence for preparing an annual report

"A work flow sequence helps you to think through every step necessary to reach your final goal. Each task in the series produces a specific result that's needed to carry out the *next* task in the sequence. See?"

"Makes sense," Joe nodded.

"Once you've identified all of the necessary steps, you can give your plan even more specificity by assigning each task a *target date for completion.* For example, a work flow sequence for creating a community teaching plan might look like this." Frank completed a second drawing and showed it to Joe. (See Illus. 5.2.)

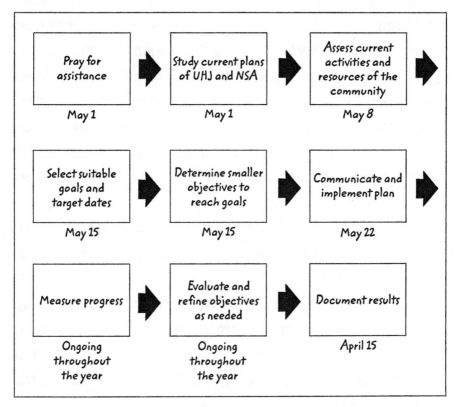

Illustration 5.2. A work flow sequence for creating a local teaching plan

"Each task has been identified and given a specific deadline for completion. And we do this with the full knowledge that each step in the sequence is essential to the overall outcome.

"Finally, no planning process is complete until you establish *clear criteria for your success.* In other words, there needs to be a consensus on what results need to be attained in order for the Assembly to feel it achieved its goal."

"I like this. But this process—it looks like it could be time-consuming if you're not used to it."

Frank agreed. "The planning process may be tedious at first, Joe, but it gets much easier with practice. And it's worth the effort. Don't forget, you get a 500 percent return on your planning investment! What's essential is having a clear vision of what you want your Assembly and your community to accomplish within a specified period of time. After all, it's much easier to plot a specific course if you have a clear destination. Which is another reason why we have to stay close to the writings, especially those of Shoghi Effendi. The Guardian gives us a clear and tangible vision of what we're striving to create in the world."

Joe leaned forward in his chair. "That reminds me of the old saying, 'If you don't know where you're going, you'll wind up somewhere else'!"

"That's right. When we stay close to the writings, we always know where we're going. We have a definite vision of humanity's future. What each Local Assembly has to determine is how much and how fast can *our* community contribute towards making that vision a reality?

"By setting challenging goals—both short-term and long-term—establishing priorities, and making realistic plans for achievement, we can do great things in our local communities!"

CHAPTER 6

The Purpose of Measurement

J oe looked thoughtfully at the work flow sequence Frank had sketched for developing a local community teaching plan. "I know you just sort of did this off the top of your head," Joe said, "but I have a feeling you've actually created a teaching plan using these steps."

"Oh yeah. With the exception of a few minor details, we've done it just like this."

"Good. Then maybe you wouldn't mind saying just a bit about this task here." Joe pointed to one of the boxes.

"Measure progress?" said Frank, reading the words beneath his finger. "What can I say? It's important that you compare how you're actually doing against the goal you've set for yourself. Otherwise you don't know if you're getting better, worse, or just standing still." He shrugged. "You've got to measure."

"Yes, but . . ." Joe hesitated. "Some people don't like to measure. Measuring means quantifying things—it's so cut-and-dry. Some people even say it's not spiritual, that it's too cold and mechanical."

"Not spiritual, huh?" nodded Frank. "If I may be honest with you, Joe, it sounds to me like those people are just afraid of objectively facing the results of their efforts."

"Well, can you blame them?" Joe persisted.

"I guess not. Nobody likes to fail. But one of the surest ways to fail is to not measure—to work in the dark."

"I guess you're right. But how do we get past the discomfort so many people have?"

"We shouldn't be scared of measurement," Frank explained. "It's a normal thing to do. In fact, anywhere you look we're surrounded by measurements.

"We all use clocks, calendars, and speedometers. We measure ages, heights, weights, and blood pressure. Without measurements like these, we couldn't understand and communicate in precise terms. Measurement is the way we see how we're doing."

Frank continued. "There are lots of ways to measure, but in general when we measure we assign a number to something according to a rule. When we measure distance, for instance, the rule says we use meters, centimeters, kilometers, and so forth. We assign numbers to distance so we can express the size of something or indicate how far away one point is from another. If we don't assign precise numbers to these ideas, we have no way of knowing where we are now or what resources we need to get us where we want to be.

"We can also use those numbers to communicate precise information to others, including those who can help us achieve our goals. Finally, we can use the information obtained through measuring to adjust or make changes in our efforts so that we are always making progress.

"So, we measure our efforts

1) *To understand our work processes and see how we're progressing,*
2) *To communicate this information to others, and*
3) *To make improvement.*

"If you don't care how you're doing, if you don't plan to tell anybody how you're doing, and if you don't care about improving— then there's no need to measure."

"Wow! That certainly doesn't apply to the Bahá'í Faith, does it?"

"It sure doesn't. We're trying to build a new world order as quickly as possible. We *have* to know how we're doing, we have to *communicate* our results to one another, and we have to *get better* at it!"

Joe made a note in his pad. "Makes sense. So what are the best things to measure in our work?"

Frank returned to his work flow sequence. "Of course, it begins here—with the selection of your goals and objectives. As I mentioned before, the planning process is incomplete until you establish clear criteria for success. In other words, it's important to have Assembly consensus on what *specific* results must be seen before you can say you've successfully achieved your goal.

"For example, if the Assembly says it wants 'more firesides than last year,' will it be satisfied with *one* more? Or does the Assembly feel there need to be at least *ten* more firesides to demonstrate progress? If it sets the goal of 'significant participation in Fund contributions,' what does the Assembly consider significant? Twenty percent? Forty percent? Maybe even sixty percent is still too low in some people's minds. If the Assembly doesn't specify and agree on its criteria for success, there will always be disagreement during the measurement and evaluation stages.

"Once you identify exactly what results you want, there are many ways to measure your progress. You can measure the *final outcome* of your activity or process, such as the average number of people attending the Nineteen Day Feast each month. You can measure against *established administrative procedures*—that is, whether things were done according to specified guidelines, such as whether a committee meets your criteria for properly organizing itself and conducting its meetings. You can measure the quality of the *facilities or equipment* the community uses in its activities, or you can measure the level of *training and knowledge* the believers have on a certain subject. You can measure based on *deadlines, budget requirements*—all sorts of things. If you can clearly describe your desired result, you can measure it. The key factor is to determine which measurements will prove most helpful in your efforts to clearly understand what's happening, to communicate this information to others, and to make improvement."

"So," Joe reasoned, "what you're saying is that when we set a goal for a 'quality' proclamation, for example, we need to determine exactly what our *requirements* are for a 'quality' proclamation—the kind of program, the type of location, how many people we want in attendance, what kind of refreshments, and so on."

"Right. And most important is for the Assembly to reach consensus on those points so that when the event is later evaluated, there'll be agreement that, 'yes, it was a quality proclamation,' or 'no, it wasn't.' That's why your criteria must be specific, measurable, and agreed upon at the beginning—so that you can properly measure and evaluate later.

"Now, you also want to be able to communicate how you're doing to others—especially the people involved in helping you achieve your goals. Whenever possible, our Assembly likes to supplement our oral and written reports with visual representations. We find that it helps people to better understand the results. Three kinds of visual representations that we use quite often are the *pie chart, the run chart,* and the *bar chart.* Here, I'll show you."

Frank took out a fresh sheet of paper and began sketching.

"*Pie charts* show the relationship of all the parts to the whole. The whole is represented by the circle, while the parts are represented by the sectors of the circle. So, for example, a pie chart could be used to show how the monthly Fund contributions are allocated in a local community. Like this—" (see Illus. 6.1)

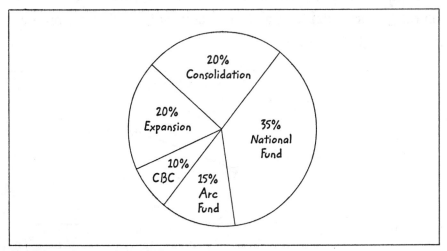

Illustration 6.1. Sample pie chart

"*Bar charts* are basically a set of parallel rectangles whose lengths represent quantities for easy comparison. For example, if we wanted to compare the average number of believers currently attending the Nineteen Day Feast to the number attending at this same time last year, it might look like this." (See Illus. 6.2.)

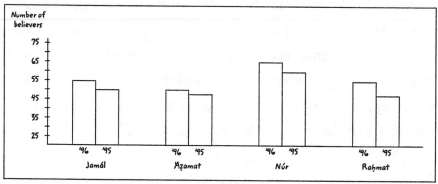

Illustration 6.2. Sample bar chart

Frank continued to speak as he drew one more chart. "*Run charts* show a set of points representing certain data which are connected by line segments. Run charts are most often used to show trends. So we might show the trend of enrollments by representing the years on the x (horizontal) axis and the number of enrollments on the y (vertical) axis." (See Illus. 6.3.)

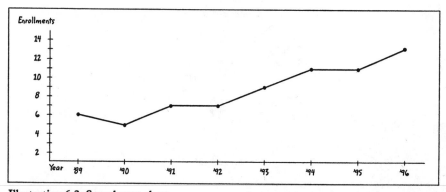

Illustration 6.3. Sample run chart

"So, Joe, how do you feel about measurement now?"

"Real good. And I think the community will feel more comfortable, too, if it's explained to them the way you just explained it to me. Once you know exactly what you want, there's only one way to be successful: Plan your work, measure your progress against your desired results, and keep working and measuring until you hit your target.

"Thanks, Frank!"

Joe took his notepad to the next Assembly meeting. Over the next few weeks the Spiritual Assembly of Somerset carefully evaluated its goals and objectives, re-prioritized its activities, and began to make clear, well-developed plans for the community's success.

For the first time in a long while, the planning process was actually *fun*—and very enlightening for the Assembly. Members of the Assembly came away from the process excited and with a clear vision of where they wanted the community to go and what it would take to get there.

But a few weeks into implementing their new plan, Joe once again called on Frank Lane.

"We have to talk, Frank."

"Joe, what's wrong? Is the Assembly struggling with their planning?"

"Oh, no! We've done some great work in establishing goals and developing our community plan. But one thing that's become clearer to us than ever is that the Assembly won't be pursuing these objectives and accomplishing all these great goals by itself. We'll be enlisting the help of the community members for virtually everything."

"That's true. The believers are the Faith's primary resource."

"But how do you coordinate all of them?" Joe asked dubiously. "I mean, how do you keep track of everything and everybody? It's practically a full-time job to juggle everything that has to be done when you're working with so many different people and projects."

"In other words, how do you successfully *manage* the process?"

"I think that's our dilemma right now," Joe concurred, feeling relieved that Frank understood. "Any suggestions?"

"Just one," Frank replied. "Koichi Nakaguchi."

Joe thought he detected a hint of amusement in Frank's voice. "What's that, some new corporate management fad?"

"No," laughed Frank. "It's the name of a man on our Assembly. Mr. Nakaguchi is a wonderful Japanese believer who owns a small bookstore on the college campus here in town. He ran a major corporation in Japan before retiring here in the States. He's our resident management expert. I'll bet he can help you. Besides, J.T. told me to pass his name on to you the next time we spoke."

"J.T.? You've got to be kidding me."

"Nope. Just carrying out instructions." Frank chuckled. "That J.T.'s pretty sharp, huh?"

"Hmmm," replied Joe.

CHAPTER 7

Managing for Results

H ere you are."

"What's this?" asked Joe, looking at the steam rising from the bowl of cloudy liquid.

"Taste it," said Koichi Nakaguchi. "You'll like it."

Koichi Nakaguchi was in his late sixties, but his smile and dancing eyes made him appear much younger. "Go on—try it!"

"Well . . . don't I need a spoon?"

"No spoon," said Mr. Nakaguchi. "Drink this way." He placed a thumb and forefinger on each side of the bowl and lifted it carefully to his lips.

Joe Strong did the same and tasted the liquid. "Mmmm. This is *delicious*. What is it?"

"Miso soup," replied Mr. Nakaguchi. "My wife's own recipe. In fact, here she is now. Eriko, come meet our guest!"

A small, delicate woman dressed in jeans and a sweatshirt appeared from an unseen hallway.

"Eriko, this is Mr. Joe Strong. He is one of the Bahá'í friends."

"Pleased to meet you, Mr. Strong." The woman nodded politely.

"Pleased to meet *you*," said Joe, smiling. "The miso soup is wonderful. Are you also a Bahá'í?"

The woman smiled shyly. "Oh no! I'm not Bahá'í. *Episcopalian*!" She seemed to laugh as she left the room.

Mr. Nakaguchi leaned towards Joe and gave him a secret wink. "She's not a Bahá'í . . . *yet*! I've been working on my wife for twenty-five years. Someday she'll be Bahá'í. I'm sure."

Joe smiled assuringly.

They carried the bowls of soup from the kitchen counter to the dining room table and sat down facing each other.

"So," began Joe, "I know your community is very successful at achieving its goals. In fact, I heard that during the Six Year Plan, Bakersfield won all of its local goals within the first year. Is that true?"

"Well . . . I have to admit it is!"

"Wow! With that kind of success, a lot of the goals must have been fairly simple ones, huh?"

"Actually, no," replied Mr. Nakaguchi. "Some of them were pretty challenging for us."

"So how did you do it? What's the secret?"

"Secret? I'm not quite sure what you mean."

"Well, for example," explained Joe, "in our community last year we had a great plan. We even went to the community to find out what kinds of things they thought we should do; in fact, more than three quarters of the goals came directly from them. But, you know . . . halfway through the year we realized nothing had really happened with the goals. I mean, there was token movement here and there, but by and large no one was really working on them. In addition, a couple of our committees weren't functioning, and the ones that *were* meeting seemed to be pursuing activities totally unrelated to the goals in our plan. At Feast, there was consultation, but it was about totally different ideas and *new* things to do. It was as if we had no plan at all."

"How did that make you feel as an Assembly?"

"Well, frustrated. I mean the Assembly spent a lot of time preparing that plan; it was the *community's* plan. But at that point we felt as if the Assembly's work had been a waste of time. We don't want to see that happen again. Your treasurer shared a lot of good ideas about goal setting. We're off to a great start. How do we make sure things turn out different this time?"

"Well," began Mr. Nakaguchi, "as you realize by now, it starts with the goals themselves. Our local goals are always based on the National Spiritual Assembly's current plan. With few exceptions, we don't pursue anything as an institution if we can't tie it in some way to the National Assembly's directives. After that, once the plan has been set, as an institution we don't entertain anything new until we feel we've done everything humanly possible to achieve the goals. We're really dogmatic about that and very committed. Even at the Feasts, we focus community consultation on the goals first. Of course, there's lots of room for individual initiative if people have other things they want to do, but we feel it's the Assembly's job to marshal the community's collective resources to focus on the goals that we believe will propel the community forward. If any new ideas pop up, we simply record them for follow-up at a later time; after all, we don't want to lose a good idea, but we don't want it to sidetrack us, either! That Plan you referred to—the one in which we achieved all of our goals in the first year—taught us a great deal. There was no doubt that it was successful because we focused exclusively on the established goals until they were well in hand. The Local Assembly's commitment was the key."

"I see what you mean. Commitment is important; I admit we could definitely improve there. But it seems to me that even commitment still needs to be supported with some solid knowledge about *how* to effectively manage the people and resources to get things done."

"You're right," agreed Mr. Nakaguchi. "I notice you brought a pad and pen—good. There are seven basic functions of good management, Joe. I'm going to give you a year's worth of business school in five minutes! Are you ready?"

As Mr. Nakaguchi spoke, Joe's pen started across the page.

"I'll give them to you in order. The seven basic functions of management begin with:

Planning. If you've talked to Frank Lane, you know that you have to be able to articulate your goals clearly, write them down in simple language, and make them measurable. Many problems on Assemblies arise from the fact that they don't take time to effectively plan their work before they begin. The goals are fuzzy or unclear. We get so caught up in the day-to-day activity of the community that we seldom ask, What exactly are we trying to accomplish? Where do we want to go, and how are we going to get there? What results are we trying to achieve, and

and what outcomes do we want? If we were to achieve our goals exactly as we want, what would they look like? What is our criteria for success; that is, how would we be able to tell we were successful? If you plan well, you save tremendous time and resources in execution.

"After you make your initial plans, the next step is

Organizing. Once you determine what you want to accomplish, you then have to identify all the resources you will need to achieve your goal. Having great goals and objectives is important, but they're only a prelude to the real work. Now you must think through your plan and acquire the people and material resources needed to do the job well. What kind of talents and skills will you need to achieve your goals and objectives? How much will it cost? Where will the money come from and what are the things that can go wrong? Make a list of the tasks and activities that must be pursued to meet the goal, and organize the list in terms of priorities. Then go back and organize the list in terms of time and sequence—the work flow sequence (see Illus. 5.2, page 49) is a perfect tool for this. Once this is done, you can begin executing your plan.

"The third basic function of management is

Personnel Selection. This is where you carefully select the individuals who possess the necessary skills you previously identified. This is one of your most important tasks as plan managers. It's been said that 95 percent of success in management is in the selection of the proper personnel. And almost all problems in business are people problems that go back to poor decisions that were made in the selection process. That's why our Assembly makes a point of personally meeting with all new enrollees as well as with those believers who transfer into the community from other areas. It helps us learn about them, and it also opens a line of communication. That way, when it comes time to look for community members to take on certain roles and responsibilities, we've got a pretty good idea of the types of resources available to us.

"In addition, here is a point that is often overlooked in the personnel selection process but must be given special attention. Whenever you appoint a committee, team, or other group to carry out an assignment, be sure to include at least one *champion* among their number. Otherwise you are very likely to end up having to personally push and prod that group from beginning to end. What is a champion? A champion is an individual who is: *committed* to seeing the assigned task through to completion, *reliable* in carrying out responsibilities, and *capable* of getting a job done in spite of the inevitable glitches and snags that almost always arise at some point in the process. A champion will not only identify problems, but he or she will also take the initiative to come up with solutions. In addition, ideally, a champion needs very little or no supervision.

"Every team needs at least one champion. If your community appears to be short on such individuals, begin immediately to work with and cultivate those believers who appear to have the potential to *become* champions!

"The fourth essential skill in management is

Delegation. This is the key skill required for the Assembly to get the maximum amount of work accomplished in the shortest possible time, and it's the most important technique in management. It's not enough to pick the right people; you have to put them in the right places and then see that they get the job done on schedule. Delegation enables the Assembly to leverage its resources and get an enormous amount of work done through the organization, deployment, and allocation of the community's resources. But remember that delegation is not abdication; the Assembly is still accountable for the final result.

"In delegating tasks to others, remember that the only true predictor of performance is past performance. It's not what a person thinks or says they can do but what they have done in the past. Of course, we always want to help community members to gain experience and grow with new responsibilities, and it's futile to look for perfection. However, you must carefully think through how the person has performed with previous responsibilities before delegating anything important.

"When you delegate a task, always

a. Give authority commensurate with responsibility. There are decisions to be made in carrying out any assignment; the people to whom you delegate responsibility must be given the power and freedom to make those decisions.

b. Give the individual or responsible party the time and resources necessary to do the job properly.

c. Set a deadline for every task that you delegate. If it's a large task to be accomplished over time, set sub-deadlines at regular intervals as well. And

d. Take time to review what you want done with the individuals to whom you delegate. Even the most conscientious and sincere person can misunderstand instructions. They will hear something you didn't say and not hear something you did say. Whenever possible, delegate responsibilities in writing; but even then, take time to meet with the individuals and ensure that they know exactly what is to be done, how it will be measured, and the deadline for completion.

"And remember: You can't hold people responsible for their results if you dictate methods. Focus instead on the desired results, give them clear requirements, then let them determine how to best achieve those results and meet those requirements. Give them a chance to let their creativity and ingenuity come out!

"The fifth function of management is

Supervision. Supervision is when you check with the group or individual on a regular basis to be sure they are on track with the assigned task. Whenever possible, set up a regular schedule of meetings to review progress. Watch for unexpected problems and delays, and be sensitive to the possibility that the job may be more than the individual(s) can handle. Be prepared to secure additional resources so that the group can stay on schedule.

"The basic principle of supervision is to *inspect* what you *ex-*

pect. You don't want to continually look over people's shoulders, but it's important to check regularly to see how things are going. To accomplish this our Assembly does two things. First, each of our committees and task forces has a specific Assembly member who acts as their liaison. This Assembly member keeps the rest of the Assembly informed of the committee's needs, plans, and so on. Second, we meet with each of our committees and task forces regularly. In fact, as soon as all of the committees are appointed, we call them together in one large meeting to review each other's mandates and discuss ways to dovetail efforts and work together on common objectives. This way, every committee knows what every other committee is working on. Just before Riḍván, we call everyone together one last time for a big appreciation dinner.

"Studies show that workers consider a task to be important to the degree that the boss asks about it on a regular basis. As an Assembly, we feel our job is to always know the status of the critical tasks for which we are responsible. We've learned to ask for and receive accurate answers to questions about status.

"Another important part of supervision is this: it is essential to avoid becoming the victims of *reverse* or *upward delegation.* Upward delegation is when the people to whom you've assigned a task delegate the task back to you. They ask you to handle some aspect of the assignment—make a few calls, obtain some information, or do some research on this or that. A lot of times they come to the Assembly with a problem and ask if the institution could consult on their concern and come up with a solution for them. Before you realize what's happened, they're free of all responsibility, and the job once again belongs to the Assembly! Many Local Assemblies find themselves working long hours on tasks they had originally assigned to their committees and task forces but which somehow got reverse-delegated back to them. Unless there is a serious problem, you should refuse to take it back!

"The next function of management is

Measuring. You've already learned about the importance of having clear requirements and objective standards of performance. An Assembly needs to agree in advance on what specific results are desired and on how success will be measured. If you agree on how success will be measured, and if you use the numbers objectively to determine how well a job has been done, you are less likely to get involved with personalities when problems arise. Instead of placing blame, you can simply refer to the agreed upon criteria for success and focus the discussion on the job rather than on the individuals.

"The seventh and final basic function of management is

Reporting. Everyone has to report their results to someone. For example, a Local Spiritual Assembly communicates with its local community and with its senior Bahá'í institutions, such as the National Spiritual Assembly and the Auxiliary Board members. In a similar fashion, the committees and members of the community are expected to report their results to the Local Assembly.

"When it comes to work situations, people don't like surprises, mainly because surprises rarely bring good news. If our committees anticipate a problem of any kind, we encourage them to report it in advance so that there are no surprises if the problem materializes, and our Assembly does the same in communicating with the community. We've also found that the discipline of reporting makes us more effective overall. The very exercise of preparing accurate analysis and reports helps us to better understand our work and to improve our performance. The very best Assemblies I have seen are very knowledgeable and precise about the results of their efforts. They measure them continually."

Joe looked over his notes. "*Planning, organizing, personnel selection, delegation, supervision, measuring,* and *reporting.* Whew! It's all here! When you said 'a year's worth of business school in a few minutes' you weren't kidding! This is great!"

Mr. Nakaguchi stood up from the table. "You know, Joe, earlier you asked about a 'secret.' There are no secrets in what I just shared with you. Any good management program will teach you those things. But our Assembly did learn something else about managing for results. I think it may be that *secret* you're looking for."

Joe leaned forward attentively.

Mr. Nakaguchi continued. "In theory it's quite simple, but in practice . . . well, let's just say it took our Assembly a long time to recognize that goal achievement really comes down to two simple words: reliability and self-discipline. We found out that without these two, nothing works."

"*Reliability* and *self-discipline,*" repeated Joe. "When it comes to a Local Assembly, what exactly do you mean when you use those words?"

"Ah, now you're asking the right questions," smiled the old businessman.

"Oh, yeah. You guys have definitely taught me that if everybody isn't using the same language from the start, minor misunderstandings can grow into big problems!"

"You are correct," Mr. Nakaguchi nodded. "Okay. So here's how we define the terms:

Reliability, essentially, is doing *what* you say you're going to do, *when* you say you're going to do it.

Self-discipline is doing what you know you should do, when you should do it, *whether you feel like it or not!*

"The terms are different," added Mr. Nakaguchi, "but they are definitely related. You can't be reliable until you master self-discipline.

"Our Local Assembly discovered that it had to model reliability and self-discipline in meeting its own commitments. First, this meant that the individual Assembly members had to be reliable in carrying out their assigned tasks; and, second, the Assembly as an institution had to become disciplined in meeting its commitments to the community. A part of that commitment involved helping the community to develop a collective self-discipline—by keeping it on track, helping the believers to focus on the current goals, and by our consistent monitoring of the goals to successful completion. Whenever the community came together to consult, we made sure it always consulted first and primarily on the goals. We consciously helped the community to gather its resources and focus its thoughts and efforts *like a laser.* Once we had disciplined ourselves and the community to do that, we began to see results almost immediately. But it isn't always easy. If you let down your guard for a second, you can get sidetracked. It takes discipline.

"There's an old saying, Joe: There are no bad soldiers under a good officer. We realized that the Assembly had to set the standard. And I'll tell you something else: The members of the LSA are subject to life's surprises just like everyone else. Our children get sick. Our cars break down. Basements flood, and individuals lose their jobs. When it comes to trouble and tribulations, we are all truly born equal, so the Assembly members stumble through life just like everyone else. But, Joe, the institution is still on call!"

"So what you're saying is that when an individual Assembly member isn't able to fulfill his or her commitment, it's up to the institution to make sure the task is covered."

"Exactly. We discovered that, as an institution, we couldn't let the changes and chances of life deter us from either our immediate purpose or our long-range plans. Otherwise, nothing ever got done."

Joe made another note in his pad.

"Just remember," Mr. Nakaguchi added, "the goal-setting process isn't simply an exercise to show how thoughtful, analytical, and efficient we can be. Goal-setting should be the first step towards achievement. Follow up with commitment, reliability, and self-discipline—and the desired results *will* come!"

CHAPTER 8

Why Are Things Slipping Through the Cracks?

A few weeks had passed when Joe Strong felt the need to make a trip to the campus bookstore after work to see Mr. Nakaguchi. By the time he arrived, it was nearly 6 P.M. Mr. Nakaguchi was standing in the doorway of his shop, talking with a young woman Joe presumed to be a local student.

"Mr. Strong, how are you?" Mr. Nakaguchi greeted him and shook his hand. "Here's someone I'd like you to meet. This is our Bahá'í sister Melanie Grant."

"Oh, how nice. Alláh-u-Abhá," said Joe. "It's a pleasure to meet you."

"Alláh-u-Abhá," said Melanie Grant. "So, you're Joe Strong. I've heard a lot about you."

"Oh really?" said Joe, a little surprised.

"Yes," said Melanie. "I serve on the Bakersfield Assembly with Mr. Nakaguchi. By the way, he was my Bahá'í teacher!"

"Melanie declared as a freshman," said Mr. Nakaguchi with a hint of pride in his voice. "This is her senior year. We're going to miss her when she graduates."

"Not as much as I'll miss you guys." Melanie smiled. "Anyway, someone mentioned your name at our last meeting. I guess you've been talking to some folks about Assembly effectiveness."

"As a matter of fact," said Joe, "that's why I dropped by. I've got another question."

"Ah," said Mr. Nakaguchi. "The answer is Amelia."

"But I haven't asked you the question."

"Oh, you're right," said Mr. Nakaguchi. "That was rude of me. Please ask your question."

"Well," said Joe, "the situation is this. We've got tremendous goals now. Seeing how to identify the most important things, establish clear requirements, and organize and plan our work has made us mighty ambitious, I'll tell you! We're more *committed* than ever, too, and we're starting to get a handle on effectively managing our resources to get the goals accomplished. But remembering to get everything done—both collectively and individually—is getting to be a bigger and bigger problem. We start our meetings by looking at our unfinished business from the previous meeting or the new items that have been added to the agenda, and we forget to follow up to see if our *previous* decisions are being carried out in a timely manner. In fact, half the time we don't know if they're being handled at all! Heck, we're making decisions so fast now, a lot of things are slipping through the cracks. Do you have any ideas on what we can do to avoid that?"

Mr. Nakaguchi seemed to seriously ponder the question for a moment. Then he smiled. "One suggestion: Amelia Edwards."

Joe nodded knowingly. "Now I've got it. Let me guess—J.T?"

Mr. Nakaguchi shrugged. "She told me to give you Amelia's name. You want to know how to keep track of all your action items and make sure they're addressed; Amelia is your answer. She's the keeper of our facilitation list."

"Your what?" puzzled Joe.

"Our facilitation list. It's the tool we use to monitor ourselves and make sure that—well, as you say—make sure that nothing 'slips through the cracks.' But I'll let Amelia explain. Here's her phone number. She's busy with graduate school, but she'll make time for you. She's expecting your call."

Joe scratched his head in bewilderment. "How could she have known . . ."

Melanie smiled. "Isn't J.T. amazing?"

CHAPTER 9

The Facilitation List

"Sorry I'm late," said Amelia Edwards. She sat down in the armchair across from Joe, her hair still wet from the shower. "I should have known I'd be cutting it a little too close if I went jogging before you got here."

"It's quite alright," said Joe. "So, you're a runner?"

"Hardly," laughed Amelia. "My friends say that when I run I look like a woman falling out of a tree—I've got such lousy form! But I started running to lose weight. And it's working. I've lost thirty pounds in six months. Not bad, huh?"

"That's tremendous!"

"I'm in graduate school full time—social psychology—and I wasn't taking very good care of myself. But I'm a very goal-oriented person. Once I realized what was happening to my health, I decided what I was going to do about it, set a target date for achievement, and took off running—literally! I suspect that's why the Assembly made me the keeper of our *facilitation list*—I like setting deadlines and getting things done!"

"That's exactly what I want to hear more about," said Joe, and he flipped open his notepad. "Tell me about this ... 'facilitation list.'"

Amelia picked up a file folder from the coffee table and removed a sheet of paper. "It's quite simple. The Assembly needed a convenient way to keep track of the tasks it assigned to individual Assembly members. Of course, the information was recorded in the Assembly's minutes, but looking through several sets of minutes to remember what was to be done by whom and by when was anything but convenient. The facilitation list solved the problem. At a glance we could instantly keep track of progress—or the lack of it—and take whatever measures were necessary to see all of our assignments through to completion. Here's a copy of the form we use."

Joe studied the form. (See Illus. 9.1.)

Amelia continued. "We hole-punch the individual sheets and keep them in a three-ring binder. The first column," she explained, "is for the *date* the task is assigned. For us, that's usually the days when the Assembly meets. The second column records specifically *what* is to be done. The third column records *who* is going to do it. The next column is the *due date for completion,* which is determined through consultation by the Assembly. The last two columns are left blank until the task is completed. At that point, the fifth column is used to record the *actual completion date.* We like to compare the target date to the actual date of completion to measure how well we meet our own deadlines and commitments. The last column is for any *comments or notes* relevant to the particular assignment."

"And this asterisk?" asked Joe, pointing to the notation in the upper right corner.

"Oh, yes. In most cases the Assembly members have the pre-

LSA Facilitation List

*–task should not be delegated to a nonassembly member

Date	Task or question to be resolved	Assigned to	Date to be completed	Actual completion date	Comments

Illustration 9.1. Local Spiritual Assembly facilitation list

rogative of enlisting the help of others from the community in carrying out their work. If a task is of a sensitive or confidential nature, however, it's noted with an asterisk—that means that the Assembly member to whom it's been assigned has to handle it personally. Here's a partially completed page from our current binder.
There's nothing confidential here; take a look." Amelia handed Joe
the page. (See Illus. 9.2.)

"My job as keeper of the list is to maintain it. We start each
Assembly meeting by reviewing all of the action items due on that
date. If anyone is having a problem with an assignment, they let the
Assembly know at that time whether they need help. If so, we reas-
sign it or do whatever it takes to get it done. Then, as the Assembly
meeting progresses, one of the chairperson's responsibilities is to
point out when something should go on the list. Of course, if she
forgets, someone else—usually me—will remind the Assembly that
a certain item has been overlooked and needs to be included. One by
one, all of the meeting's action items are recorded on the list.

"It's also great to have the list when we can't remember something, such as whether a particular task was assigned or a specific
due date set. With the facilitation list there's no more poring over
old minutes. It's a great overview of the Assembly's work during
any given period of time."

"This is fantastic!" exclaimed Joe. "It's like a mini-filing system, except it's for the current items—the action stuff! We can put
this to use immediately!"

"Oh, we love it," chimed in Amelia. "Now over here, using the
same principle but in a somewhat different manner, we created this."
She reached into her folder, pulled out another form, and handed it
to Joe. "It's a *loan log.*"

LSA Facilitation List

*task should not be delegated to a non-assembly member

Date	Task or question to be resolved	Assigned to	Date to be completed	Actual completion date	Comments
May 14	Draft letter to Mayor's office re: proclamation	Farhad	May 21	May 21	Letter approved for mailing.
May 14	Update community mailing list	Richard	May 21	May 28	Richard left town on business for a week.
May 21	What does Shoghi Effendi say about tie votes in a Bahá'í election? Need to research!	JT	June 4		

Illustration 9.2. Partially completed facilitation list

"This looks interesting," said Joe.

"We found that we were making loans to believers and then we'd forget that we'd done so. Much later, someone would remember, but we couldn't remember the conditions we had established for paying the loan back. It was a real mess, and it was a serious problem because we were dealing with the Fund."

"So you created this?"

"Right. This is a very simple form for recording loans."

Joe studied the form closely. (See Illus. 9.3.)

RECORD OF ASSEMBLY LOAN

Name of borrower: _____

Address: _____

Phone(s): _____

Date of decision:_____ Date of loan:_____ Amount: _____

Circumstances:

Conditions for repayment:

Record of repayment:

Date	Amt.		Date	Amt.		Date	Amt.
____	____		____	____		____	____
____	____		____	____		____	____
____	____		____	____		____	____
____	____		____	____		____	____

Illustration 9.3. Record of assembly loan

"The loan log is kept by the treasurer. We also make a note on the facilitation list to check the status of the loan by a certain date.

"While we're at it, you might find this one of interest, too." She handed him the last piece of paper from her folder. "This one is a tool we developed for recording notes at the Nineteen Day Feast."

"I like this already," said Joe, taking the form.

"When our general secretary is at the Feast, we can count on a pretty standardized format for reporting what happens. But if he isn't there, or if it's one of our smaller neighborhood Feasts, which we plan occasionally, someone else takes notes and, well, let's just say it used to be a frustrating experience for the Assembly to piece things together."

"Um, neighborhood Feasts?" Joe interrupted. "That's not a term I'm familiar with."

"Oh—good question!" Amelia paused momentarily to reflect on how best to explain. "Well, we have a relatively large community in Bakersfield," she started. "It's not easy for some of the friends to come to a central location for Feast each month. So the Assembly divided up the city map into four 'neighborhoods' and assigned roughly an equal number of believers to each area based on where they lived. Now, three or four times a year, we designate the Nineteen Day Feast as a neighborhood Feast, and the four areas meet separately. Of course the neighborhood Feasts are much smaller, but there's also a more intimate feeling. People seem to enjoy the change of pace."

"I see," said Joe.

"So, as I was saying," Amelia continued, "we came up with this form. Now everyone uses the same recording device, regardless of whether it's another Assembly member substituting for the secretary at the community Feast, or if it's a neighborhood Feast and notes are being taken by the host or hostess. You can have this copy if you like."

Joe studied the form in more detail. (See Illus. 9.4.)

```
┌─────────────────────────────────────────────────────────┐
│              NINETEEN DAY FEAST REPORT                   │
│                                                          │
│  Date_____ Feast of_____ Location ____│
│  Number in Attendance                                    │
│  Adults_____Youth (age 15–20) _____ Children (14 and under) _____│
│  Recommendations to the Spiritual Assembly (community vote taken)│
│  1.                                                      │
│  2.                                                      │
│  3.                                                      │
│  Suggestions to the Spiritual Assembly (no vote taken)   │
│  1.                                                      │
│  2.                                                      │
│  3.                                                      │
│                                                          │
│  Miscellaneous notes                                     │
│                                                          │
│  Submitted by: _____  │
└─────────────────────────────────────────────────────────┘
```

Illustration 9.4. Nineteen Day Feast report

"Of course these are just the forms we use," Amelia added. "Feel free to customize any of them to fit your needs. Or create new ones of your own."

"You have no idea how much I appreciate this." Joe smiled as he made a neat stack of all the form samples. "I'm sure we'll put all of these to good use."

"It's our pleasure," smiled Amelia. "But, Joe . . ."

"Yes?"

"Well, you know of course that none of this is set in stone. I mean it's not like it's an official part of Bahá'í administration. These forms are effective in keeping our Assembly on track and moving forward, and everybody on our Assembly likes them—so we use them. Your Assembly may find other ways to do the same thing."

"Oh, yes. Of course. I understand." (Joe did understand, but he was starting to wonder if every Bakersfield Assembly member had been given the same script before meeting with him.)

"Well, I don't mean to rush us, but I'm meeting some Bahá'í friends for dinner and a movie. Maybe you'd like to join us."

"Thanks, but my wife is holding my supper for me, and this is a Cub Scouts night; got to get my son there on time. But I really enjoyed meeting you."

"Likewise. Oh, before I forget—" Amelia looked through the papers scattered on the coffee table, "I have something for you."

"Oh?"

"Here it is." She handed him an envelope.

In the car, Joe opened the letter-size envelope. Inside was a folded note. It read:

> Hello Joe Strong!
>
> Hope you're doing well. What did you think of our facilitation list? If you're interested, our recording secretary would be happy to talk with you about an effective filing system. His name is Richard Lauden. Give him a call at 227-8889.
>
> Best wishes,
> J. Tucker

Joe chuckled in spite of himself. "This is like a scavenger hunt!"

CHAPTER 10

Creating a Filing System

J oe Strong stood at the front door, staring at the man staring back at him from across the doorsill.

"We've met before," they said simultaneously.

"Your eight year old plays in the YMCA soccer league," said Rich Lauden.

"And your daughter plays for the YWCA team," Joe replied. They both laughed.

"I didn't think there were any other Bahá'ís in the league," said Richard. "I wear my Bahá'í T-shirts to all the games."

"I like to put Bahá'í books on the dashboard and in the rear window of my car, hoping somebody might notice and maybe ask a question!" They both laughed again.

"Well, this is funny. Come on in."

Richard walked Joe past the foyer and through the hall leading to his study. "That's my wife in the first photo on the wall; there's my daughter, who you've seen before, and my six year old, four year old, and six month old." They reached the den, which was large but crowded with oversized cushions, a computer on a wide desk, two chests of toys, a file cabinet, three walls of books, and a large cage. "Don't worry," said Richard, noticing that Joe was eyeing the cage cautiously. "That's just a pregnant guinea pig. What you need to look out for is the snake."

"The snake?"

"Yeah. The kids usually keep it in an aquarium in their room, but it got out a week ago. I think it's crawling through the walls somewhere, but—"

"I hate snakes." said Joe.

"Me, too," said Richard. "Good riddance!"

Joe quickly made the decision to sit close to the door. "I guess you know why I'm here."

"Files."

"So, what can you tell me?"

"Well, not much, Joe. As recording secretary of the Assembly, I keep the records up-to-date. I inherited a system that's embarrassingly simple. I'm sure you could come up with something better. The only reason I haven't changed it is because . . . it works."

"If it's effective, I'm interested."

"Okay then." Richard made a sweeping gesture with his hand. "The computer and the file cabinet are in this room, so this is where I do my Assembly work—at night when the kids are in bed. Doing the minutes and filing has almost become a meditation! It's the one time of day when I feel like there's any order in my life!"

They walked over to the file cabinet. "We started out with all our records in stacked storage boxes, but soon got this metal file cabinet. It was a good investment.

"A long time ago, the Assembly decided that simple was best for us. The file at the very front of the top drawer is an index to all the other files; anyone can find what they want whether I'm around to help them or not." Richard opened the top drawer and pulled out the index.

"It only takes a second to understand how our system works," he explained. "One way to file is alphabetically. Like I said, from time to time other members of the Assembly need to use the files when I'm not around. If the filing system were alphabetical, people might not understand how things have been filed—you know, since there can be different key words used in placing the files. Also, when a file is returned, some people don't like to have to think about how to alphabetize it back in order. So, instead of alphabetizing the files, we *numbered* them. They're grouped together in broad categories. The index in the top drawer lists every file in sequence according to its number and grouping."

Joe looked at enough of the index to get a clear picture of Richard's system. (See Illus. 10.1.)

"Hmmm. What happens," Joe queried, "if you decide to add a file between categories?

"Good question. If additional files are needed in a particular category, I decide which existing subject file is most closely related, then use that file number along with an alpha code. For example, as you can see here, one grouping we have is that of *Incoming Correspondence* from Bahá'í Institutions and Agencies. Copies of messages from the Universal House of Justice is file number 2, the Continental Board of Counselors is number 3, the National Spiritual Assembly is number 4, the Auxiliary Board is number 5, and other

```
INDEX
No.    File Name
1A     LSA Minutes—1993–94
1B     LSA Minutes—1994–95
1C     LSA Minutes—1995–96
1D     LSA Minutes—1996–97
2      Incoming Correspondence—Universal House of Justice
3      Incoming Correspondence—Continental Board of Counselors
4      Incoming Correspondence—U.S. National Spiritual Assembly
5      Incoming Correspondence—Auxiliary Board
6      Incoming Correspondence—other local Assemblies
7A     Local Teaching Plans—1993–94
7B     Local Teaching Plans—1994–95
7C     Local Teaching Plans—1995–96
7D     Local Teaching Plans—1996–97
```

Illustration 10.1. Sample of Bakersfield Assembly's filing system

Local Spiritual Assemblies is number 6. If we needed to add a new file, such as correspondence from the National Teaching Committee, we would probably group it with the National Assembly's file and code it as number 4A.

"We also use a file marker system to keep track of files that have been removed or 'checked out.' It's just a big yellow file folder with the word REMOVED written on it.

"When someone removes a file, he or she puts one of these yellow folders in its spot with a note inside saying which file was removed and who has it. We've also put instructions in the file index folder to remind people to do this."

"You know, I like this," said Joe. "I like this a lot."

"There must be a hundred kinds of filing systems. This is what we do. Of course, it doesn't mean *your* LSA will like it or that it will work for *you*. Any questions?"

Joe didn't have any questions, but by now he was getting tired of the same disclaimer every time someone showed him something new. He closed his notepad. "So how's your daughter's team doing this year?"

"Six and 0 on the season so far," Richard beamed. "How's your son's team?"

"Zero–5 and 1," Joe frowned. "Who's coaching that YWCA team now, anyway?"

CHAPTER 11

So *That's* What She Does!

Richard and Joe looked for each other at the soccer games. They sat together and cheered for one another's kids. Their wives met and became friends, too. The families had a lot in common.

Joe's son even found the missing snake while playing with the Lauden kids in their attic.

And the two families got together at the annual area-wide Ayyám-i-Há party, which, coincidentally, was being hosted by the Bakersfield community.

"By the way," Richard said as they were whisking the children from the pin-the-tail-on-the-donkey game to the puppet show about pioneering, "how are things going on the Somerset Assembly now? It's been a couple of months since you first talked to J.T., hasn't it?"

"Yeah, it has. And things are actually going quite well. You folks passed on some tremendous tools for increasing our effectiveness; you can't imagine how it's helped us. But—why are you asking? *Did Julianna give you a name to pass on to me?*"

"A name?" asked Richard. "I don't understand what you mean."

"Never mind," said Joe, smiling. "But now that you mention it, I guess there is one small issue."

"What's that?"

"We really are doing very well in terms of getting things done. But . . . well, there's just so much on our plates now. We never seem to have enough time to do everything we need to do during our meetings. But, hey, I guess that's par for the course, as they say. There's not much we can do about the time crunch at this point in the Faith's growth, right? The needs of the Cause just keep expanding."

"Well, that's true. But have you talked to J. T. about that? You know, she's got some real strong ideas about that sort of thing—*time management,* I mean. She's a consultant for some of the biggest companies in the Midwest. That's her field, you know."

Joe stopped in his tracks. "Time management?" he echoed. "So *that's* what she does!"

The next day Joe called Julianna from his office. It was around 1 P.M. The phone rang twice, and then a brisk voice answered at the other end.

"This is Julianna Tucker. I've got exactly three minutes to talk to whoever you are!"

"Wha, uh . . . Ms. Tucker—Julianna? This is Joe. Joe Strong."

"Joe?" Her voice softened. "Well how are you? It's been a while since we've spoken."

"I've got just two words for you," Joe whispered. "Time management."

"You caught me," Julianna laughed.

"Why didn't you tell me your expertise was in time management?"

"Joe, I thought it was most important for your Assembly to figure out what it wanted to do first. For time management to be really effective, you have to have something to organize your time *around*. After all, the primary purpose of time management is to make sure you have the time to devote to the things that are most important to you; I suspect your Assembly knows what those things are now. So why don't we get together and talk about time management?"

CHAPTER 12

Time Management

Joe rang the front doorbell twice, but there was no response. He was just about to press the button a third time when he heard the latch turn. The door opened and Julianna stood beaming in the entryway. "Sorry," she offered with a gentle smile. "Come on in."

"For a moment I thought maybe I had the wrong day or time."

Julianna seemed a little embarrassed. "I apologize. I was finishing the Long Obligatory Prayer."

"Oh, I'm so sorry. I should wait outside—"

"No, no—I finished. I was just afraid I'd be too tired to give it my full attention when I got home late tonight." She paused as they walked down the hall. "You know, Joe, I do think it's my favorite of all the prayers!" She took a deep breath. "*So*, can I get you something to drink? Are you hungry?"

"No, thanks, I'm fine," said Joe.

They sat down in her office.

"So, Joe, since we first spoke have you picked up any ideas your Assembly can use?"

"Are you kidding?" Joe laughed. "Tons of them. We've definitely learned that busy doesn't necessarily mean effective *or* productive. And we know now how important it is not to confuse *activity* with results, or *motion* with accomplishment. We've seen what a difference effectiveness makes in the progress of the community!"

"Well, all the tools you've adopted, from the structuring of your agenda, to the facilitation list, to the monitoring of your committees, are *all* time management devices—ways to free up more of the Assembly's time to focus attention on the high priority tasks. But there could be a few more specific things you might want to consider to free up even more of your meeting time for doing the things you most want to do.

Utilizing *Event Checklists*

"Did Amelia tell you about the facilitation list?" Julianna continued.

"Oh yes. She swears by it."

"You're telling me. I don't think she ever lets it out of her sight! But I have to admit, if you use it the way it's intended, it works like a charm! It's really made a difference in our Assembly's effectiveness in following through on its decisions."

"It's had the same impact on our Assembly!"

"And I'll bet she showed you the loan form, too, didn't she?"

"Yes. At this point, we don't make many loans, but I can see it coming in handy in the future, especially when our community grows larger in size and we have people coming to us with all kinds of needs. She also showed me the form you use for recording attendance and recommendations at the Feast. Our Assembly put that one to use immediately."

"She showed you that, did she? Boy, she's stealing my thunder." Julianna picked up an accordion file and pulled several official-looking pieces of paper from it. "But I'll bet she didn't show you these."

Joe leaned across the desk to get a better look. "What are they?"

"Just a few special-event checklists used by our Assembly, but they really help us to save time." She spread the lists out across the desk blotter. "This idea has proven to be invaluable to our Assembly. One of these checklists can be handed off to a committee or task force—even a single individual—and you can be confident that none of the fine details involved in the planning and execution of one of these important activities will be missed. We have five basic checklists that we use most often: one for proclamation events, one for weddings, one for meeting with new believers, one for the annual election meeting, and one for funerals."

"*Funerals?*" Joe echoed with surprise. "You're kidding, right?"

"No." Julianna extracted it from the small stack of papers. "In fact, this one might be the most helpful of all. You mentioned it yourself once; when someone in the community dies, it's a shock, and sometimes it's hard to think clearly. There are often special circumstances, and things happen so quickly that it isn't always practical for the Assembly to meet as a body to discuss the various details. After dealing with that kind of situation a few times, we put together this checklist for coordinating a funeral. It's really come in handy. But here, you can have a copy of each of these. They may give you some ideas for other kinds of checklists that would be helpful to your Assembly or community."

Joe examined the five checklists. (See Event Checklists.)

Checklist for a Proclamation Event

Determine nature of the program
— What is the objective of this event (i.e. why is it being held and what result do you want)?
— Analyze your audience. Who are you hoping to attract? What is the most effective way to present the Faith to this group?
— Will there be a single speaker or more than one? How long will s/he speak? Will the talk be followed by a question and answer period?
— Who will serve as master of ceremonies? What will be this person's responsibilities?
— Will there be music? What type? Who will provide it? At what point in the program?
— Will there be any other type of entertainment?
— Will there be a separate program/activity for children and/or youth?
— Will there be a printed program? Who will prepare and approve it? What is the cost? Who will copy and make it available at the event? How will it be distributed?
— Will you invite other Bahá'í communities to participate? How will this be done? Who will handle this responsibility?
— Will you invite any special guests (e.g., public officials, people of prominence)? How will this be done? Who will be responsible for this?

Determine nature of hospitality
— Who will set up the room/site (appropriate tables, chairs, staging, microphones, etc.)? At what time should the room be ready?
— Will the room be decorated? In what manner? Who will be responsible for this?
— Will refreshments be served? What type? Who will prepare and bring?

— Who will arrange and serve them at the proclamation site? Are special serving supplies (dishes, utensils, etc.) needed? What are the associated costs?

— Will there be a guest book? Who will obtain and bring it to the event? Who will see that guests sign the book and that the book is retrieved at the end of the event?

— Will there be individuals appointed to serve as official greeters? What will be their specific responsibilities?

— Who will clean up after the event? Who will coordinate this?

Determine date, time, and location

— What is the most suitable location/environment for this event? What is the best time and date? What costs are involved?

— What time will the location be available for set-up? When must the event end and the location be vacated?

— Should a specific person be identified to act as a liaison with the owner(s) of the location? What will be this person's responsibilities and authority?

Advertising

— How will this event be publicized? Who will coordinate the publicity? Are funds needed and, if so, how much will it cost?

Miscellaneous

— Will Bahá'í literature be made available at the event? What type? Who will obtain it? What is the cost and how will it be paid for? How will it be made available/displayed at the event?

Budget

— Add up the projected costs. Is sufficient money available? If not, how might it be obtained? Is it necessary to adjust the plans based on financial considerations?

Management

— Who will manage this event, insuring its successful completion? Is this

person /group reliable? Have they demonstrated mature experience and commitment in handling other responsibilities in the community?
— What type of supervision will this individual/group require?
— What will be the procedures for reporting?

Checklist for Bahá'í Weddings

Planning

— Determine whether a liaison between the couple and the Spiritual Assembly is needed/desired.
— If bride and/or groom is Bahá'í, ensure that they are registered believers in good standing. If the Bahá'í is unknown to the Assembly, verify membership and status with another Local Assembly or the National Spiritual Assembly. Also, if previously married and the individual(s) was a Bahá'í at the time of the divorce, verify that a Bahá'í divorce was granted.
— Advise the couple of the laws and principles of Bahá'í marriage: parental consent, the vows, the need for two witnesses, the simple nature of the ceremony, the absence of commingling of religious traditions.
— Ensure that consent from all living parents has been freely given and obtained in writing. If there are special circumstances in this regard, determine how the matter will be resolved and inform couple.
— Obtain a Bahá'í marriage certificate.
— Determine from the couple the date, time, and location of ceremony.
— Review program planned by couple. If bride or groom is not Bahá'í, ensure that they have not commingled the Bahá'í ceremony with any other religious ceremony. If a second ceremony of another religion is desired, ensure that both ceremonies will be conducted on the same Gregorian day and that the two ceremonies are not commingled.
— If the Bahá'í ceremony is to be the legal one, ensure that the civil license has been obtained. Ensure that all requirements for civil law (e.g., blood tests) have been satisfied and that any required paperwork has been submitted before any specified deadlines.

— Appoint or ask the couple to name two witnesses to be present at the ceremony. The witnesses must be acceptable to the Local Assembly; if Bahá'ís, ensure that they are registered believers in good standing.

— Appoint an Assembly representative to attend the wedding.

— Have the couple obtain marriage license from the county clerk's office. Be sure they take notice of any restrictions or guidelines.

— If bride and/or groom is Bahá'í, complete for each believer a Bahá'í Membership Data Form, including name(s), any change of address, and marriage license number.

— Is the LSA providing any other assistance with the program? If so, what type?

— Ensure that someone at the ceremony (e.g., the Assembly representative) will be responsible for either returning the license to the Assembly or making copies and mailing the original to the county clerk's office. (See below, "After Ceremony".)

During or immediately following ceremony

— Have Bahá'í marriage certificate completed and issued to the couple. (Copy for the Assembly's files, if desired.)

After Ceremony

— Mail the completed Bahá'í Membership Data form(s) to the Bahá'í National Center within a few days following the ceremony.

— Complete marriage license according to instructions provided. Provide the couple with a copy, retain a copy for the Assembly's files, and mail the original to the county clerk's office.

Checklist for Preparing New Declarants for Enrollment

In meeting with the newly declared believer, review the following subjects
to ensure that the individual has a *basic* understanding of Bahá'í teachings
and principles in preparation for enrollment.

1. The station of
      Bahá'u'lláh
      The Báb
      'Abdu'l-Bahá
      The Guardianship—Shoghi Effendi

2. Laws and ordinances
      Daily prayer, including the Obligatory Prayers
      Fasting
      Abstention from alcohol and drugs
      Moral rectitude

3. Bahá'í Administration: the role and authority of
      The Local Spiritual Assembly
      The National Spiritual Assembly
      The Universal House of Justice

4. Bahá'í Community Life
      The multifaceted diversity of the Bahá'í community
      The Nineteen Day Feast
      Holy Days
      The importance of individual participation
      The Bahá'í Funds (Local, National, Continental, and International)

5. Question and answer period

Checklist for the Annual Meeting

Planning
— Has the National Spiritual Assembly or other senior institutions provided a special message to be shared and/or consulted upon at this meeting?
— Will there be an annual report from the Local Assembly? Will it be distributed to the community before or during the meeting? Who will be responsible for this?
— Prepare and approve the meeting agenda. Arrange to have copies for all attendees.
— Will there be a special role in the program or any other activities for children? Youth? Who will plan and coordinate this?
— Determine meeting location, time, and date.
— Update the voting list.
— Prepare and mail the election call to all voting members.
— Select chief teller and assistants.
— Prepare instructions for tellers and provide in advance.
— Gather materials for the tellers: tally sheets, pencils, eligible voter list, etc.
— Prepare devotional program.
— Will there be music? At what point(s) in the meeting?
— Will there be additional readings on the nature of Bahá'í elections?
— Will there be refreshments? What type? Who will provide them and at what point in the meeting will they be served?
— Will there be a photographer for community and/or Local Assembly photographs?

Immediately prior to the meeting
— Secure any last minute absentee ballots and present to the tellers.
— Verify the presence of all readers, presenters, tellers, children's program teachers, etc.

Immediately following the meeting
— The individual elected with the highest number of votes should gather

the newly elected members of the Assembly and choose a date, time, and location for the first meeting and the election of permanent officers.

Meeting follow-up
___ Formally report election results to the community.
___ Send completed election information to the Bahá'í National Center.

Annual Meeting Sample Agenda

6:45 P.M.	Music as community gathers
7:00	Welcome by Chairperson
	Opening prayers and devotional readings
7:15	Reading of messages from the senior institutions
7:30	Reading of the Local Assembly's Annual Report
7:45	Call for election
	Introduction of tellers and instructions on voting procedures
	Prayers for the election of the Local Spiritual Assembly
	Voting
8:15	Consultation on the past year
	Suggestions and recommendations to the incoming Local Assembly
9:00	Tellers' report and approval by the community
	Refreshments and fellowship

Checklist for Bahá'í Funerals

First priorities
— Establish contact with the deceased's family. Consult with them regarding relevant Bahá'í laws, the funeral arrangements, and any other assistance they may require.

— Is there a will? Who is the executor? If a will exists, make provisions to have it read as soon as possible following notification of death.

Preparation of the body and burial arrangements
— Select a funeral home and review with the management the Bahá'í laws regarding preparation and burial.

— Who will prepare the body and when? Who will secure the necessary materials (e.g., burial ring, burial cloth, washing supplies, etc). What costs are associated, and who will pay?

— Is a burial plot available for purchase or has one been prearranged? What costs are associated, and who will pay?

The funeral service: program content and related issues
— Who will arrange and coordinate the program?

— Will a history of the deceased's life be shared? Who will prepare this? Who will deliver it at the service?

— Which Bahá'í writings will be used? In addition to the Prayer for the Dead (the reading of which is obligatory for believers over the age of 15), which Bahá'í prayers will be included in the program?

— Will other religious or secular writings be used?

— Will there be music? What type, who will provide it, and at what point will it occur in the program?

— Is a chairperson or master of ceremonies desired?

— Will there be ushers at the service?

— Who will be asked to read at the service?

— Who will be asked to serve as pallbearers?

— Will there be flowers from the sponsoring Bahá'í community or institution?

— Will specific individual(s) be asked in advance to share remembrances?

— Will spontaneous remembrances be encouraged?

— Will there be a program at the graveside?

— Will there be a guest book at the service?

— Is the proper manner for reciting the Prayer for the Dead understood? Who will read it?

— Are there any announcements or acknowledgments that need to be made? Who will prepare and deliver them?

Funeral service: printed program

— Will a history of the deceased's life be printed in the program? Who will gather the information and prepare it? What will be included (e.g., work/occupation, date of enrollment, nature of Bahá'í service, etc.)?

— Will Bahá'í writings or any other religious or secular writings be included?

— Is a photo of the deceased to be included?

— Who will typeset/prepare the printed text? How will it be copied?

— Will a statement of thanks from the deceased's family, sponsoring institution or community be printed in the program? What will it say?

— Will the readings/prayers to be used in the service be referenced in the printed program?

— Will there be a reception following burial? If so, will it be announced in the program?

Miscellaneous issues

— Who should be notified concerning the believer's passing, and how will this be done? Who will handle this?

— Who will write the obituary and/or supply personal data to the funeral home?

— Is the deceased of a stature that the Baha'i National Center or Bahá'í World Center should be notified immediately?

— Who will notify the Bahá'í National Center's department of membership and records and *The American Bahá'í* or other appropriate Bahá'í publications?

— If there will be a reception following the burial, who will plan and coordinate it? Where will it be held? Will there be refreshments? How and when will this be announced? What cost is involved and who will pay?

__ Will there be a visitation prior to the funeral service?

__ Will the sponsoring institution send thank-you notes to individuals who assisted in some way with the service or other aspects of the funeral arrangements? Who will coordinate this?

The Community Resource File

"Yes. I would definitely like to take these back to my Assembly," Joe commented after reviewing the checklists. "Thank you!"

"Sure." Julianna pulled four more sheets of paper from the folder, three of which were stapled together. "Another area that used to slow us down was identifying believers to appoint to certain tasks; you know, committee membership, special projects, and the like. The problem was obvious: We didn't have a handle on our most valuable resource—*the community members themselves.* Who are the experienced speakers in the community? Who are the talented musicians? Who wants to work in public relations? Who's qualified to conduct an audit of the Assembly? Who likes working with children? A lot of the time we were guessing. So, we consulted about it and came up with a solution. First, we began meeting with both new enrollees and those believers who transferred in from other communities. Since they were new to the community, they were the immediate challenge because we knew the least about them. Then we developed a simple community resource file." She handed him the pages. "We have each believer or family complete this three-page form. Then we collate the information on separate topic sheets. Both the individual forms and the topic sheets are kept in a three-ring binder. Again, these are samples you can keep if you like."

Joe looked over the three-page questionnaire and the sample topic sheet Julianna gave him. (See Illus. 12.1 and 12.2.)

Bahá'í Community Resource Profile

Name _____

Address _____

Home phone (   ) _____

Occupation _____

How long? _____

Work phone (   ) _____

Are you willing/able to accept Bahá'í related calls at your
(circle one or more): Home?   Work?

Spouse (if applicable)

Name _____

Occupation _____

How long? _____

Work phone (   ) _____

*Who (other than your spouse) should be contacted in the event
of an emergency?*

Name _____

Address _____

Home phone (   ) _____ Work phone (   ) _____

Relationship _____

Illustration 12.1. Bahá'í community resource profile

Bahá'í Community Resource Profile

Children/Youth (if applicable)

Name   Age   School/Grade

_____   ____   _____

_____   ____   _____

_____   ____   _____

_____   ____   _____

_____   ____   _____

_____   ____   _____

Please list any special interests or extracurricular activities your children enjoy.

_____

_____

_____

_____

_____

_____

Bahá'í Community Resource Profile

Talents, Skills, and Special Interests

In this section you are asked to share which of the following subjects apply to you. Please check (✓) as many categories as you wish, but only those you feel most strongly about. Providing this information does not commit you to any particular activity or service.

Definitions

Know a little: You have some knowledge of this subject but not enough to serve as a leader or teacher of others, OR you have limited hands-on experience.

Know a lot: You know enough to lead or teach others. OR you have enough knowledge that you would feel confident serving as a consultant to others. People in this category are usually professionals or have carried out considerable studies either in school or as a hobby, or have attained a level of expertise through hands-on experience.

Like to learn: You would be interested in joining a study group, attending a workshop or lecture, or otherwise participating in some type of learning activity related to this subject.

	Know a little	Know a lot	Like to learn
Animals/Pets	☐	☐	☐
Art	☐	☐	☐
Athletics/Sports	☐	☐	☐
Banking/Finance	☐	☐	☐
Carpentry	☐	☐	☐
Children/Youth	☐	☐	☐
Computers	☐	☐	☐
Construction	☐	☐	☐
Cooking	☐	☐	☐
Crafts	☐	☐	☐
Dance	☐	☐	☐
Drama/Theater/Film	☐	☐	☐
Education	☐	☐	☐
Electronics	☐	☐	☐
Exercise/Fitness	☐	☐	☐
Foreign Language	☐	☐	☐
Games/Recreation	☐	☐	☐

Illustration 12.1. Bahá'í community resource profile

Bahá'í Community Resource Profile

Talents, Skills, and Special Interests

	Know a little	Know a lot	Like to learn
Gardening	☐	☐	☐
Health Care	☐	☐	☐
History	☐	☐	☐
Home Improvement	☐	☐	☐
Law	☐	☐	☐
Literature	☐	☐	☐
Mechanics	☐	☐	☐
Music	☐	☐	☐
Nutrition	☐	☐	☐
Photography	☐	☐	☐
Planning/Coordination	☐	☐	☐
Psychology/Counseling	☐	☐	☐
Public Speaking	☐	☐	☐
Real Estate	☐	☐	☐
Seniors	☐	☐	☐
Travel	☐	☐	☐
Writing/Editing	☐	☐	☐

Other *(please explain)* _____

Please use this space for additional comments:

(Please print your name here for identification purposes)

Bahá'í Community Resource Profile

Please list your Bahá'í experience (e.g. personal projects, service on Local Spiritual Assemblies or Bahá'í committees, pioneering, etc.). Include years of service where applicable.

_____

_____

_____

Please list any community organizations or social service agencies with which your household is currently involved. What is your level of involvement?

_____

_____

_____

For which of the following groups would you be willing to serve as a community resource contact? (Circle all that apply.)

A.   Agencies of the local Bahá'í community (i.e., the LSA, its committees, special task forces, etc.)

B.   Individual community members seeking personal assistance

C.   Groups and individuals organizing social activites or those who are interested in networking.

D.   Other *(please explain)*

E.   I prefer not to be contacted at this time (i.e., within the next 3–6 months)

Additional Comments:

_____

_____

_____

Name: _____

Signature: _____ Date: _____

Illustration 12.1. Bahá'í community resource profile

Bahá'í Community Resource Profile Carpentry		
Know a little	*Know a lot*	*Like to learn*
Arthur Jones	Mary Allen	June Calhoun
Amelia Edwards	Joseph Bean	Mina Khavari
	Douglas Brewer	

Illustration 12.2. Bahá'í community resource file topic page (sample)

The LSA's Policy Log

Joe was intrigued with the possibilities as he considered how the Somerset community could benefit from creating and maintaining such records. Before he could comment, Julianna continued.

"Here's something your Assembly might want to consider to save some meeting time," she suggested. "It's an idea for a *policy log*. It would be great if we had this computerized, but for now it's just on index cards in a metal card box."

"Oh, you've lost me already," said Joe. "*What's* in the metal card box?"

"Sorry. Let me back up. Do you remember our first conversation a few months ago? You mentioned that your Assembly would occasionally establish a standing policy or practice and then couldn't remember what it was? This is our answer to that dilemma: our standing policies are collected together in this card file." Julianna retrieved a small metal box from her desk. "We have it divided into categories such as Feast, Committees, Assembly Meetings, and so forth. In many cases, we've discovered that just the act of writing up a card and filing it in the box is enough to make us remember the policy without having to look it up every time. In any case, we always have one place to look for our policies where we know we'll find them. Believe me, it saves a lot of time that we used to spend looking through old minutes." Julianna flipped through the cards and handed a small number of them to Joe. "Here are a few sample cards from our file."

REGISTRY OF MARRIAGES AND FUNERALS

The LSA will maintain a **registry of marriages and funerals** conducted by this institution. This registry will be the responsibility of the Recording Secretary.

Assembly meeting date: 10/7/94

MEETINGS WITH INDIVIDUALS, GROUPS, OR OTHER LSA'S

After any **meeting with an individual, group, or other Local Assembly,** and after this Assembly has its own follow-up consultation, the guest(s) or other parties will be sent a written summary of the points of the meeting along with a restatement of any agreements and/or subsequent decisions made by this Assembly.

Assembly meeting date: 9/26/95

INCLEMENT WEATHER

Re **inclement weather:** If the Bakersfield School
District cancels school due to inclement weather on a
night when a community-sponsored event is scheduled
(i.e., feast, deepening, fireside, or holy day observance),
that event will automatically be postponed, and the
rescheduled date will be publicized through the
community's phone tree and on the Assembly's voice
mail message. On weekends, the events will be held as
scheduled unless notification of postponement is
announced via the phone tree and the voice mail
message.

Assembly meeting date: 12/1/96

Important versus Urgent

"Having to rethink past decisions definitely consumes time that could be better utilized," continued Julianna after Joe handed the policy cards back to her. "But there's something else that we find occurs much more often and is much more costly to us: interruptions."

"Interruptions?" Joe probed.

"Oh yes! We start out with important goals and priorities and with every intention of achieving them in a timely manner. We know it's important to do them, but somehow we just don't get to them. We're distracted, interrupted, or have to drop everything because some crisis arises or there's some problem that has to be solved *now*. Suddenly something urgent has appeared at the top of our agenda, and we have to drop everything else to deal with it. What was once 'important' has been knocked out by the 'urgent.' Sound familiar?"

"Oh yes," Joe nodded.

"It's the old *demands of others* syndrome. It's a precarious balance, to be sure; you have to be responsive to the needs of individuals while staying on track with your established priorities.

"What we eventually came to realize is that there's a major difference between something that's *important* and something that's *urgent*. The dictionary defines important as *'having great worth, significance, or influence,'* while it defines urgent as *'something that calls for immediate attention.'*"

"Of course, there are times," Julianna continued, "when an unexpected crisis or problem presents a genuine emergency. In that case, it's imperative that the Assembly rise to the occasion and handle it. After all, that's why the Assembly is there, especially when it comes to the well-being of the believers. There's no room for wavering on that point! At the same time, while it may be impossible to prevent every emergency, if your pattern is that of running from one crisis to the next, you can do irreparable harm to other projects and long-term plans. You lose control of your own priorities and end up reacting to events instead of making them happen."

Joe opened his notepad. "I have a feeling your Assembly has come up with an idea or two."

"A few suggestions, yes. Much easier to say than do, I'll admit, but with a little effort they're fairly simple to implement. Here are five ideas we've taken advantage of:

1. Use your meeting agenda to schedule your own major projects and complete them in a timely manner. Remember: Anything important that you *delay* will eventually reach a crisis stage.

2. When urgent matters arise, don't simply react. Give yourself time to think about the best, most appropriate course of action.

3. Anticipate unforeseen problems, and make provisions for handling them if they should occur.

4. Avoid the impulse to 'drop everything' in order to handle the crisis immediately. Oftentimes it's far more important to complete the task you're working on and *then* take the time to think about and solve the unexpected problem.

5. If something unexpected comes up, write it down and look at it in relation to the other items you already have on your agenda. If the new issue is not as important as some others (and it often isn't), put it on your agenda with the date it arrived and assign a need-to-handle-by date. Proceed to complete the more important project(s) you're working on, and then address the new item(s).

"The key," Julianna explained, "is that you have to set your own priorities; don't let others set them for you. If you want to prevent yourselves from being sidetracked, you'll have to fight for it. That's why you have a carefully thought out agenda."

Choosing between Alternative Solutions

Joe sat back in his chair. "This is a little bit off the subject, but another thing we've found that challenges us is that when the Assembly has a decision to make, consultation *usually* reveals the right course of action. But occasionally the right choice isn't so clear. Sometimes it can take quite a while to make the right decision, especially when there is more than one reasonable option."

Julianna nodded. "I know what you mean. And I don't think it's off the subject at all. We've found a technique that helps us clarify our thinking in situations like that—you might want to try it, too.

"We use a sheet of paper or put up a large sheet of flip chart paper. Someone acts as scribe and writes the decision being considered across the top of the page and draws a line down the middle. Then we carefully list the *positive aspects* of the decision on one side and the negative aspects on the other. We try to list everything we can possibly think of. Then we evaluate the positives and negatives in relation to *any relevant spiritual principles, what's best for the individual(s) involved,* and *what's best for the Faith.* We then make our decision. Oftentimes, the process of simply listing all the various pros and cons will make the best decision obvious.

"We also use this technique when we need to choose between *several* different options. Using a separate sheet of paper for each option, we proceed in the same manner. Then we determine which option is most appropriate in light of our evaluation of all the positives and negatives."

"Hmmm. Good ideas. But tell me," Joe prodded, "does this always work?"

"No, not always. Occasionally we get *really* stuck. When that happens we may address the same topic several meetings in a row and not make any real progress. It's rare, but it happens."

"What do you do then?"

"In those kinds of situations, we've found that it's best to take an extended break." Julianna smiled.

"What do you mean?"

"Sometimes the Assembly will go for a walk outside. Or we

may play a short interactive game of some sort to relax a bit. It's the old left brain, right brain principle. For bigger or more numerous issues, we may even schedule a retreat of one to several days; that can be very effective. The change of scenery coupled with the change in our normal meeting routine always seems to kick-start us. We go away for a brief period, make our decisions, and come back. Sometimes we find that having a change of pace along these lines is the most important thing we can do before making a decision. It works for us; try it sometime."

Some Timesaving Tips

"Here are a handful of unrelated ideas that should also save you considerable time in your work.

- Always establish clear mandates for your committees and task forces, and put them in writing. The mandates should include specific requirements and measurable tasks, making clear what results they are to try to obtain and the standards those results should meet.
- Following a by-election of the Assembly, have two Assembly members (such as the chairperson and secretary) meet with the newly elected member outside of your normal Assembly meeting to brief them on current procedures such as the meeting format, the roles of your officers, hot projects, and to give them background information on upcoming agenda items. Also use that time to pass on any responsibilities that the individual(s) may need to assume immediately.
- In planning the meeting agenda, schedule your top priority

tasks so that they are addressed during the Assembly's peak energy periods or *prime time*. In other words, recognize the Assembly's energy levels, and do the most important work when the Assembly is at its best. When does your Assembly function most effectively? Are your most productive hours early in the meeting, near the middle after a little warm up, or late in the session? For most Assemblies, prime time is at the beginning of the meeting, immediately following prayers and preliminary business. In that case, you would make a special effort to get what you most want to accomplish out of the first hour of the meeting. For example, items that call for creativity might be placed early on the agenda; items based more on basic principles and administrative procedures might be saved for the end.

- As each new agenda item is taken up by the Assembly, the chairperson should succinctly state the purpose or the *desired outcome* of the consultation. In other words, why is the item being addressed by the Assembly? What specific question needs to be answered, issue resolved, decision made, and so on? You may find it helpful to identify the desired outcome on the agenda next to the topic. If for some reason the desired outcome is unclear at the time the agenda is prepared, put *d.o.* (for "desired outcome") and a blank space next to the agenda topic to prompt the Assembly to fill in the blank when the item is introduced.

- If you find that more than one agenda item can be handled simultaneously, do so.

- Certain types of letters, plans, and proposals are often easier to consult upon if the Assembly first appoints one or two individuals to prepare a draft that can later be used as a starting point for consultation by the larger body. When beginning "from scratch" as a group, such creative undertakings can be frustrating and counterproductive. The Assembly may or may not agree with the tone or general direction of the draft, but its value lies in the fact that it stimulates thought and provides an initial framework and catalyst to start the consultation moving forward.

- Learn to say "No." It's important to respond to the community's needs, but everything is not of equal importance. If you make a habit of allowing individuals, committees, and other "last-minute" additions to change your meeting agenda, you will face dire consequences in short order. Know what's important, prioritize, and make sure the *most* important things are done first.

"Whew!" laughed Joe. "I thought I'd already heard about all the time-saving devices, but this is a whole new batch of ideas that suddenly seem essential! Got anything else?"

"Just two more thoughts," replied Julianna. "This first one isn't directly related to time management, but it makes executing some of the other things go a little more smoothly. Periodically take time to note the Assembly's and the community's *successes.*"

"Their successes? You mean the things we did well?"

"Right. Do this for two reasons. First, acknowledgment of success brings confidence and validation. Use a pat on the back as a springboard for future endeavors. Second, use the opportunity to ask yourselves if there are things that you did in the past to make your efforts successful that you need to do more of in the future.

"Finally, this last thought is quite different from anything else we've discussed, but frankly it's had more of an impact on the way we operate than nearly anything else we've talked about this afternoon.

"We were having a problem distinguishing between real issues that required time and resources to resolve, and doing what we eventually came to refer to as *flinching.*"

"*Flinching?*" Joe stopped writing. "What does that mean?"

"Well, what do people do when they flinch?"

Joe thought for a moment. "It's kind of funny, but when I hear that word I think of the old cowboy movies I used to watch as a kid. When a character *flinched*, it meant he'd lost his nerve. There was usually some kind of challenge: One fellow stood his ground while the other one sort of gave in under the pressure. By flinching, he lost the challenge—and usually his self-respect."

"Exactly," Julianna nodded. "Our Assembly found that sometimes we were going around in circles on certain issues not because we couldn't come up with a solution, but simply because we were nervous about doing what we all knew should be done and lacked the confidence to carry it out. We hadn't *committed* ourselves to doing the right thing. That lack of resolve was a *flinch*. Flinches take up valuable time on our agenda because we talk about them over and over again without taking action. They also sap our confidence and inner resolve because we repeatedly fail to do what we know should be done.

"The large-scale teaching event we repeatedly postponed because deep down we were afraid of failure; a long overdue, uncomfortable meeting with a certain believer regarding violations of Bahá'í law; the proclamation to the City Council that we kept saying we'd do but never seemed to get around to—all flinches!"

"What did you do about it?"

Julianna took a deep breath. "We had to face the music. You can't build the new world order running backwards, Joe. This Cause is about courage and faith. If you know a certain course of action is the right thing to do, don't back off and don't retreat. Don't yield ground, turn aside, or be deflected from doing what you know is best for the Faith. It's become our motto now, Joe: *Don't flinch!*"

Julianna looked at her watch and stood up. "Here I am, talking about time management, and I'm almost late for my next appointment. I do hate to rush, but you know how it is sometimes!"

"Yes, of course, I understand." Joe closed his notepad and stood up.

"Remember, Joe: The Assembly must choose how it will spend its time. Make that choice with thought and purpose, because the second that just slipped by . . . is gone forever!"

They started down the hallway towards the front door. "By the way, Joe, I'm sure you understand that this is just the way *we* do things. We might do something different in a few years—or even a few weeks. It's not Bahá'í law or anything like that. You do understand that, don't you?"

Joe was definitely tired of hearing every Bakersfield Assembly member repeat those same peculiar words of warning. "Yes, yes, I understand that," he said a little impatiently.

"Great. Call me back in a few weeks and let me know how you're doing!"

CHAPTER 13

A Rash of Problems

Rich Lauden was in Somerset on business early one afternoon, so he stopped by Joe's office to see him. Joe was just about to run errands during his lunch hour, so he invited Rich to ride along.

"I'm really sorry I've had to cancel our getting together twice in a row this month," Joe apologized. "My kids were really looking forward to visiting your gang. But lately our Assembly has had to deal with a rash of personal problems in the community. To keep from falling behind in our regular agenda we had to hold extra meetings to meet with all the involved parties, and then of course we needed time to consult. These kinds of things have to be handled very carefully, and they take a heck of a lot of time. But with a community your size, I'm sure you can relate to that."

"No," said Rich. "Actually, I can't."

"Well, don't you have to have extra meetings for things like that?" Joe probed.

Rich shrugged. "No. Never."

"Then how do you handle it when people want to bring personal problems to the Assembly?"

"I don't think you've met our vice-chair. Her name's Jean Barclay. Nice lady, but she always makes me a little nervous." As he spoke, Rich pulled down the passenger side visor and began looking closely in the mirror.

Joe watched him out of the corner of his eye. "What are you looking at?"

"My right bicuspid. I think I need a root canal!"

"Oh," said Joe, glancing at Rich with a puzzled expression on his face. "Did you just change the subject?"

"Huh? Oh . . . actually, no," answered Rich, closing the visor. "Jean Barclay—she's a dentist, and I'm always afraid she's looking at my teeth; silly, I know! But besides that, she's really a great person. Always calm and in control. And you know what? Jean knows everybody in the community by name—every man, woman, youth, and child—all two hundred-and-five of them. Once, when she was chairing the Feast, she had everybody stand, and one by one she introduced every person and said something about what was happening in each of their lives—you know, who just got promoted, who made the high school honor society, who's working on a master's degree—that sort of thing. Mighty impressive, I'll tell you."

"Sounds like it."

"I'm embarrassed to say I couldn't do that. Anyway, you should talk to Jean. In addition to being the vice-chair, she's also the Assembly's coordinator for our personal consultation task forces."

"Personal consultation task forces?"

"Yeah. They play a key role in the way our Assembly handles

requests for consultation on personal issues. It may be an idea whose time has come for your Assembly. But don't bother taking out your notepad just yet. I'll put you in touch with Jean, and she can tell you all about them.

"Just remember," Rich added, "don't open your mouth too wide when you're around her. After all, she's a dentist!"

CHAPTER 14

Personal Consultation
Task Forces

When Joe arrived at Jean Barclay's apartment, he was surprised to find Amelia Edwards and Melanie Grant waiting with Jean in her living room.

"Mr. Strong," said Jean, shaking Joe's outstretched hand. "It's a pleasure to meet you."

"Same here," Joe smiled.

Jean gestured toward Melanie and Amelia. "I understand you've already met my fellow Assembly members."

"Yes, I have," said Joe. "It's nice to see both of you again."

"Please have a seat," said Jean. "I have coffee on the tray here."

The four of them settled into comfortable chairs to talk.

"I asked Melanie and Amelia to join us," began Jean, "because they also work with our personal consultation task forces."

"Well, I'm glad all three of you are here," said Joe. "These task forces sound interesting. What exactly do they do?"

"Melanie," said Jean, "why don't you start while I pour the coffee?"

"Sure," Melanie agreed. "What generally happens, Joe, is that our general secretary will receive a call from an individual requesting assistance from the Assembly in a personal matter. The secretary gets the person's name and phone number and passes the information along to Jean, who assembles a task force to meet with the individual."

"The task force is usually composed of three people," explained Amelia, "one of whom is always an Assembly member. Right now the Assembly has asked Jean, Melanie, and myself to serve in this way. The Assembly tries to use other community members as much as possible in its work, and we decided that using non-Assembly members in this capacity was desirable. Because this is a special kind of work, the Assembly has carefully identified a pool of four to five community members. For example, Jean's husband is a part of this group. These are believers who have proven to be especially mature, deepened, and well respected in the community. So, when Jean needs a personal consultation task force, she pairs two of the available non-Assembly members from our pool with one of the three of us.

"The task force then arranges to meet with the party or parties to gather information. Specifically, they are to:

- Listen to the individual's concerns,
- Ask questions for the sake of clarity and understanding, and
- Restate what they've heard to ensure that they've understood the issues presented.

"The task force is also empowered to share any spiritual principles that are relevant to the concerns, but *they give no advice or opinions to the individual.*"

Jean set the cups of coffee in front of them.

"After they've met with the involved parties," Amelia continued, "the task force consults and then prepares a summary along with their recommendations for the Assembly's consideration."

"Hmmm," Joe said, sipping his coffee. "It sounds like that would save the Assembly quite a bit of extra time and effort. But could you say a little more about why you always include one LSA member on each task force? Is there a particular reason for that?"

"Yes," said Melanie. "Having an Assembly member working on each task force ensures that the process is being followed as the Assembly intended. It also makes communication and status checks easier."

"I think it's also important," interjected Jean, "to acknowledge that when an Assembly member is part of the group that meets with the individuals, the parties know that the Assembly is directly involved with their concern and that their issues and questions will reach the institution. In the future, as the community grows larger and the Assembly's responsibilities expand, this policy may well have to change, but for now it's how we do it."

"As usual, we have a form," said Amelia, laughing. "This is used by the task forces to make their reports to the Assembly. I brought one for you to take a look at."

Amelia handed Joe the form, which he looked over carefully. (See Illus. 14.1.)

PERSONAL CONSULTATION REPORT

Meeting With:
Task Force members:

Meeting date:
Issue Summary:

When does this issue need to be resolved?
Relevant spiritual principle(s):

Recommendations to the Spiritual Assembly:

Signed: _____ Date: _____

_____

_____

Illustration 14.1. Personal consultation report

"You know," said Joe after several moments, "this sounds like a great way to handle personal consultation cases on the Assembly's agenda. I'm really excited about this idea. I can't wait to take it back to our Assembly."

Jean suddenly had a concerned look on her face. For an instant Joe was afraid that she had noticed his slight overbite, but her comment had an all-too-familiar ring to it.

"Uh, Joe," Jean began in a cautious tone of voice. "You know, this is how we do it in Bakersfield. We're not experts at this. We've just tried a few different things over the years, and, well, this works for *us*."

Joe, exasperated, finally decided to say something. "You know, I have to ask you a question. Why does everybody I talk to on your Assembly keep saying that?"

The three of them looked at each other. "Keep saying what?"

"That this is *our* way and not the *only* way. That *our* Assembly likes this, but yours may not. That this isn't 'the Bahá'í way.' Why does everybody keep harping on that? Our Assembly has adopted a lot of your ideas, and they work great! But you all sound as if you're apologizing for helping us. What gives?"

"Oh, gee," Jean grimaced. "I see what you mean. Maybe we *have* overdone it with the warnings. I guess we all just wanted to be sure that you understand this is all about *unity.*"

"Unity?" responded Joe. "What do you mean?"

"Well," reasoned Amelia, "none of these tools means a thing if your Assembly members don't love each other and move forward *together.*"

"If using any of these ideas prevents that from happening," added Melanie, "it's better not to use them. Get it?"

Joe smiled, a little embarrassed, and took a deep breath. "As usual, you folks make a lot of sense. It's pretty obvious why you're saying it after you put it that way. After all this time, you'd better believe I've got it . . . but thanks for the reminder!"

"So," asked Jean, "any other questions about the personal consultation task forces?"

"No," said Joe. "I think I understand."

"Hey, before I forget—" Melanie interrupted, "did you guys hear the news? Mr. Nakaguchi's wife declared—*Eriko became a Bahá'í!*"

"No!" Amelia nearly dropped her coffee cup.

Jean leaned back in her chair. "You're kidding!"

"It happened just yesterday. Isn't that exciting? I'm so happy for him!"

Joe laughed out loud. "He said it'd be any day. Boy, that's great!"

"Wow!" said Amelia, nodding and laughing and seeming almost giddy with the surprise. "That's *really* great!"

CHAPTER 15

Something's Still Missing

The Local Spiritual Assembly of Somerset had become efficient—VERY efficient. And they were effective—VERY effective. But something still bothered Joe. Six months after his assembly had started its trek towards greater effectiveness, there was still something missing that he couldn't put his finger on. He decided to call Julianna. "Can I come by one more time?" he asked her over the phone on a Monday night. "I'm not quite sure what it is, but maybe you can help me figure it out."

"Gosh, my week is already overscheduled," Julianna sighed. "But . . . we're having the next Feast at 10 A.M. on Sunday. We're all very excited; this will be Eriko Nakaguchi's first one! Maybe you could join us and we could talk there."

Joe accepted immediately. "Great! Somerset's Feast is the night before, so I won't have to miss it. I'll bring my family with me if that's okay."

"Perfect. We're meeting at the park district building at the corner of Fifth and Grand Avenue. See you there!"

It was fortunate that Joe and his family arrived early, because the parking lot of the park district building was nearly full. On their way into the building he caught a glimpse of Eriko, her face luminous and bright, her very happy husband by her side. Inside the one-story building, the recreation room was decorated and the believers seemed to enjoy being crowded together on folding chairs and large cushions. Joe and his family arrived just in time for the devotions, and for the first time he saw a large portion of the Bakersfield Bahá'í community gathered en masse.

It was at that morning Feast, midway through the business portion of the meeting, that Joe put his finger on what he thought was missing in his own community. When the gathering broke for the social portion, Joe met Julianna at the punch bowl filled with orange juice.

"Joe!" Julianna smiled, "I met your wife and kids just a few moments ago. What a great family. You're a very lucky man!"

"Thank you. They're pretty special. And, by the way, I think this Feast and this community are pretty special, too. And being here today, talking to some folks, listening to the consultation and watching the friends interact, I think I've realized something significant."

"What's that?"

Joe sighed. "I hate to say it, but our community doesn't have the same kind of *spirit* you do here. Our Assembly is more efficient now, and we're effective, too. But there's a spirit, a certain kind of unity, missing both on the Assembly *and* in the community. At our Feasts, some people have even stood up and said we're not attractive to seekers because we don't have a better community life, that we aren't really unified. They suggest maybe the solution is to do more *social things* together. Who knows? Anyway, being here, I realize I don't know exactly what 'it' is, but you've obviously got it . . . and we don't."

Julianna was quiet for a long time.

"What's wrong?" asked Joe. "No answers?"

Julianna smiled. "Well, frankly, no. I'm stumped. Although . . ." She paused briefly, then asked, "Joe, how many of our Assembly members have you met?"

"Well, let's see. I've met Farhad, Rich, Frank, Mr. Nakaguchi, Melanie, Amelia, Dr. Barclay, and yourself."

"Hmmm. That's eight. The one you haven't met is Aunt Rachel."

Joe registered surprise. "I didn't know you had an aunt in the Bahá'í community."

"Oh no. She's not really my aunt; we just call her that because she's like family to all of us, and we love her. The reason you haven't met her is that she's often away on a traveling teaching trip of some sort. She usually gets in for Assembly meetings and for her firesides, but then—*poof!*—she's gone again! In fact, a lot of us have only gotten to know her better because we accepted an invitation to go teaching with her!"

"And you think she knows something about community spirit and unity?"

"Well," offered Julianna, "why don't you arrange to meet her? Then you can decide for yourself!"

CHAPTER 16

The Core Business

J oe placed his spoon alongside the near-empty bowl and rested his hands on the linen tablecloth. "I've heard a great deal about you, Mrs. Flippen."

"Then you must have heard that everybody calls me 'Aunt Rachel.'"

"Yes ma'am," said Joe politely, feeling just a little intimidated by this soft-spoken, radiant black woman. "I understand that your grandparents . . . were slaves?"

"That's right. As a child sitting at their feet, I heard some amazing stories."

Joe sighed with awe. "You pioneered to Africa and served on a National Spiritual Assembly there. You've taught the Faith all over the world. They tell me you even met the Guardian."

"True, true—all true. But I'm older now. I stay closer to home and try to take on fewer administrative responsibilities. Here, have some more peach cobbler."

"Oh, Aunt Rachel, I couldn't eat another mouthful. Barbecued ribs, chicken rice, fresh greens, biscuits, and homemade cobbler—I haven't eaten food this good since . . . well, never!"

"That's southern cooking, Mr. Strong, and I'm glad you enjoyed it. It's just me and my grandson living here now. But he's six feet tall, plays basketball, and runs track for the high school, so I always keep a lot of food in the refrigerator for him and his friends. He's a fine Bahá'í, too. He started a Bahá'í club at the school last year."

"It sounds like you're raising a very fine young man."

"Well," she smiled gently, "me and Bahá'u'lláh."

They left the kitchen table and carried their glasses of iced tea into the living room.

"So," began Aunt Rachel, "I understand you've been spending time with my fellow Assembly members. I'll bet they told you all about *effectiveness.* How to *save time, set goals,* and *prioritize;* and how to use your resources efficiently to get *results.*" She laughed. "Am I right?"

"Yes. That's exactly what they told me. But," Joe hesitated uncomfortably, "do you disagree with that?"

"You mean time management and effectiveness? Oh no! I'm all for it. Take our chairperson for example. J.T.'s good with time; she has to be! Did you know that in addition to running her own business and her work on the Assembly, she volunteers three days a week at the children's hospital *and* takes care of her father in the nursing home every weekend?"

"No. I didn't."

"There's a lot of things people don't know about J.T.," she

nodded. "In the same way, we Bahá'ís have to be effective in *our* work, too, because if we aren't, humanity is going suffer that much more and that much longer! No, we absolutely need to be effective. But . . . effectiveness isn't the *ultimate* goal is it, Joe Strong?"

Joe didn't know how to respond, but it didn't seem to matter. Aunt Rachel just smiled at him and continued. "I understand your Assembly has become *very* effective. So if effectiveness alone was the answer, you wouldn't be here talking to me now, would you?"

"I guess not," Joe admitted in a soft voice.

"So, what *is* the answer, Joe Strong? Why are we struggling so mightily on these Local Assemblies?"

Joe thought for several moments. He hoped Aunt Rachel would say something more, but this time she remained quiet as she looked deeply into his face, her eyes sparkling, a sweet, gentle smile on her lips. And then it struck him. *Well, of course,* Joe thought. And he said, "It seems to me—that is, everything I've read has led me to believe—that the Local Spiritual Assembly's primary role in this day . . . is to promote the teaching work."

Aunt Rachel nodded positively. "I understand you're from the corporate world, Mr. Strong. Using your terminology, you could say that teaching is the Local Assembly's 'core business.' These local institutions are to work towards bringing the Faith to wider and greater circles of humanity. We have to create opportunities for every segment of society to investigate the teachings, and we have to lead individual souls to unreservedly and wholeheartedly embrace the Faith and become active *lovers* of Bahá'u'lláh. Oh, the Assembly has many important functions—after all, 'Abdu'l-Bahá calls them the 'Trustees of the Merciful.' But this—leading the teaching work—

is its most important responsibility in this day. To effectively teach the Cause, Joe—*that's* the *ultimate* goal."

Aunt Rachel smiled mischievously. "Now, I know what you're thinking, Joe. You're thinking, '*I came to see this old woman to find out about community spirit and unity. Why is she lecturing me about teaching?*'"

"Well," said Joe, embarrassed, "I wasn't thinking that you're old, but—"

"But the rest of it is right on, isn't it?" Aunt Rachel laughed in a way that made Joe feel very comfortable. "I know, Joe, I know. So let's talk about unity and the community.

"We have a lot of diversity in our Bahá'í family, Joe. Over 2,100 different races, tribes, and ethnic groups, our writings translated into hundreds of languages and dialects, people from every conceivable background and philosophy. What holds such a diverse group like us together?"

"Our love for Bahá'u'lláh," Joe replied.

"That's right! We love Bahá'u'lláh and the sacrifice He made for humanity so much that we have allowed Him to change our hearts and to instill in us certain values that we all share. It's those shared values that keep us together and make us a community. But you know, Joe, have you ever noticed how difficult it is to just *sit around* and love each other? Outside of a few close friends and family, it's difficult for a community of *any* kind to feel close if they do nothing but visit and socialize with one another. A community has to have something to rally around. A purpose that galvanizes the people; a *vision* that gets folks to move, to lend their support, something they can get excited and enthusiastic about. That's what *teaching* does, Joe!

"'Abdu'l-Bahá said that if we're not teaching, the spirit is entirely cut off, but when we *are* teaching, miracles happen! That's what gets people excited; that's what brings the community together and keeps us united! We're conquering the hearts of all mankind with God's divine teachings. We're alleviating the pain and injustice that's built up over thousands of years, and against all odds we're building that Kingdom of God on Earth that all the Prophets in history have prophesied! What more lofty goal could there be? Where can anyone find a more glorious adventure? And that's why everything we do as institutions, all our efforts to be effective, boil down to one issue: success in teaching. Because in the end, if everything we do doesn't contribute to that process, *none of our other work is going to matter.*"

Aunt Rachel's face grew more radiant as she spoke. Joe sat with rapt attention, feeling his own enthusiasm and excitement grow as her words touched him, but as he listened he suddenly felt a wave of sadness. He looked at her solemnly. "I know you're right, Aunt Rachel, but you know what I hear at our Feasts? Sometimes people say, we aren't *ready* to teach. They say seekers will never be attracted to us until we become closer to each other. Some of them say we have to learn to love each other more, remove all our flaws as a community, before we try to give the Faith to others. And sometimes, Aunt Rachel . . . I look at our communities and I think they may be right."

"We do need to be closer and more unified," she agreed without hesitation. "We have to learn to take better care of each other, to become the close-knit family Bahá'u'lláh wants us to be. But to say we have to wait until that happens before we can teach—there's a flaw in that argument. Just consider this: What if we never become 'closer'? Does that mean we'll never teach? Maybe the soul who could become the unifying factor is just outside, waiting to be taught and brought into the community. But if we stop teaching until we become *more* this or *better* at that, we could miss the opportunity to reach that person. There's always infinite room for growth and improvement when we're trying to take on the qualities and attributes of God. But that's why the processes of expansion and deepening go hand in hand. If we stay with the Creative Word, with the prayers, and if we strive each and every day to bring our individual lives a little closer to the divine standard set for us by Bahá'u'lláh, we'll get better at it. But there's too much pain and suffering in the world these days. We can't afford to wait to be perfect before taking this message to God's people. The world needs us *now*! Besides," she gestured toward a bookcase full of Bahá'í books, "look at all these writings of Bahá'u'lláh, 'Abdu'l-Bahá, Shoghi Effendi, and the Universal House of Justice telling us to *arise*. Do you think they don't know we have flaws? Joe, we are not only going to *arise* in spite of our weaknesses, we're going to be *victorious*. That's the power of God's message. That's the power of Bahá'u'lláh!"

"I never thought of it like that," Joe said pensively. "And you're right. So, what more can the Assembly do? How do we get the believers to understand, to stop hesitating and step forward to really do this work?"

Aunt Rachel looked deeply into his face again. "You're a good man, Joe Strong. And, by the way, that's a fine name for a Bahá'í—'Strong.'"

"So I've been told," Joe laughed softly.

"You ask what more the Assembly can do. I'm going to tell you something that you may not like. A lot of people don't understand this, but I'm telling you because I believe you will understand. And then you'll know what to do."

Joe waited. Aunt Rachel looked at him a long time before speaking.

"Joe, how many of the members of your Assembly hold regular firesides in their homes?"

Joe hesitated.

"It's okay—I don't expect you to answer out loud," she said. "How many of them always attend the Nineteen Day Feast? And how many can be counted on to attend community sponsored events such as deepenings and proclamations? As individuals we can't do *everything*, but how many of your Assembly members spend far more of their time carrying out administrative functions than they spend actually participating in the activities that the institution asks the community to support?"

Joe nodded. "The LSA work does take a lot of our time."

"Of course it does. But here is a cold, hard fact: *If the individual Assembly members don't lead the way in carrying out the directives and appeals of the institution, in all likelihood a significant percentage of the community won't respond either.*

"I travel a lot, Joe. I see a lot of Bahá'í communities. And I can tell you that the most successful ones—the ones where there is a high level of participation, where there are numerous firesides and regular teaching events, the ones where deepenings and Feasts are always well attended, the ones where there is a steady stream of new enrollments—those are the communities where the individual Assembly members are the first to obey the directives and respond to the appeals of the Assembly. Now I know that the Assembly members are overburdened and overworked, and this is a heavy load to place on the shoulders of nine individuals. But right now, at this point in our development, this is the reality of the situation. If the community is going to approach its potential, the individual Assembly members have to accept the additional responsibility of being models for community participation. *Is this fair?* No it isn't, Joe. *Is it the reality?* I believe it is."

Joe was quiet for a long time before speaking. "It makes sense, Aunt Rachel. But that's a lot to ask—a lot to expect of so few."

Aunt Rachel nodded. "You're right. But human beings need models. They need people they can respect and look up to. Whether we're comfortable with it or not, the Assembly members are in many ways the models within their community. If the individual Assembly members don't hold firesides, host Feasts, participate in deepenings, carry out assignments as requested, take individual initiative, open their homes to show hospitality—they shouldn't be surprised if very few others in the community arise to do these things. We don't like the idea that people look up to us as models—that's a terrible responsibility. But it's human nature. That's why Bahá'u'lláh gave us 'Abdu'l-Bahá; He's the only *true* model. But the believers still look up to the people who serve on their institutions. They would be *honored* to sit where you sit, so in many ways they strive, both consciously and unconsciously, to follow your example. When the Assembly members fail to do the things we talk about, you may not think so, but the community is *watching.* They're aware of what the Assembly members do, their level of service in the community, and they have this image in the back of their minds when they make decisions about their own community efforts. When the Assembly members themselves fail to respond to their own appeals, it sends an unfortunate message to the community that says, *'What we're asking you to do isn't really that important.'"*

"And you've really seen it make a difference?"

"Well, you're a corporate man, Joe. Look at the numbers. If the Assembly members arise to carry out the institution's instructions, there will be at least nine regular firesides each month, at least nine people at the Feast, at least nine people at every deepening. How would your community change if there were nine regular and *effective* firesides each month, Joe Strong?"

"Quite a bit," said Joe, chuckling and nodding gently as he listened to this powerful woman who was more than twice his age and wise as the stars. "Quite a bit *indeed!"*

CHAPTER 17

The Road to Maturation: The Journey Continues

Months went by, and the Local Spiritual Assembly and Bahá'í community of Somerset continued to make great progress in advancing the work of the Cause.

It was a warm autumn day when Joe returned home from work. He planned to take a quick shower and have dinner with his family before leaving for the Assembly meeting. His wife had asked him to help her pick out new drapery for the living room first, but judging from the Assembly's recent meetings, he had a feeling he would be back *early* and in plenty of time to look through the samples she had brought home. As he moved toward the bedroom, he noticed that the light on the answering machine in his study was flashing. He pressed the playback button and listened to the message.

Hello, Joe? This is Julianna Tucker. Listen, I only have a second, but I just got a call from a young lady in Vicksburg, just ten miles from you. They've got a community of about

thirty believers, and she thinks the Assembly is having grow-
ing pains. I'm really busy this week, and I'll be traveling the
next two, and I was just wondering if . . . *your* Assembly
might have time to talk with her a bit. Maybe share a few
things that have worked for you. I hate to bother you, but if
you could do this I know they would appreciate it. Let me
know. Bye.

Joe stopped the tape and smiled to himself. "No bother at all,
J.T. If our Assembly can help in any way, it'll be our bounty!"

The Beginning . . .

Joe Strong's Checklist for
Local Spiritual Assembly Effectiveness

- Take time to list both the Assembly's and the community's past successes. Validation builds confidence.

- Prayerfully study the current messages of the Universal House of Justice and the National Spiritual Assembly, then set meaningful goals for both your Assembly and the community—goals that will move the Faith forward!

- Identify your top priorities by writing them down. Choose, and then commit.

- Distinguish between *efficiency* and *effectiveness*. Strive for both, but never sacrifice the latter for the former.

- Keep the Assembly's meeting room clean, neat, and orderly. Have Bahá'í reference materials close at hand.

- Keep a clear "Facilitation List." Commit to its use, and check items off as you complete them.

- Prepare for the *big* tasks by achieving important, confidence-building small tasks. Use these smaller projects to practice *reliability, commitment, and self-discipline.*

- Organize your work so that you are able to consult regularly and at length on *teaching.*

- Allow a specific time at your meetings for casual talk and socializing.

- Stamp out negativity in yourselves and in others. Be committed. Be passionate. Be confident.

- Establish clear and specific criteria for success for every project you undertake or delegate to others. Then be com-

mitted to monitoring and managing the project to successful completion.

- *Let go of fear.* Be exhilarated by the possibilities and inspired
  by the unfailing promises of divine assistance.
- Make a habit of carefully planning your work before you
  begin. Create a work flow sequence of the necessary tasks
  and establish a time line to take you to completion.
- Form healthy, open, and loving partnerships with your committees and any others to whom you delegate responsibility.
  Establish specific *expectations* and *requirements* for their work,
  and meet with each one on a regular basis to ensure their
  understanding and compliance. *Nurture them with love.*
- Set up a filing system that anyone on the Assembly can use
  easily.
- Be professional. Never say, "It can't be done." Be committed to doing what must be done to achieve the results you
  want.
- Stop blaming others. Resolve to learn from your mistakes.
  When things go wrong, determine what you could have done
  differently to affect the outcome. Improve your processes
  by identifying your missteps and determining to avoid them
  in the future.
- Create checklists for the recurring tasks and projects of the
  Assembly. Carefully file them so that they are readily available when needed.
- Create a simple policy file.
- Remember that the Assembly is a divinely ordained institu-
  tion. Act accordingly.
- When decision-making becomes unusually difficult: Go on

a retreat. Take a walk. Get away from your normal routine. Make your decision and come back.

- Create a community resource file. Appoint a community member to update and maintain it. Share it with your committees and agencies as needed.

- As individual Assembly members, model the behavior you wish to see in the community.

- Accept that you are *on call*. Determine as an institution that you will not let the changes and chances of life deter you from either your immediate purpose or your long-range plans.

- Seek the advice of other Bahá'í institutions. Establish relationships with your Auxiliary Board members and with other Local Spiritual Assemblies. If you learn something useful, pass it on to others.

- *Don't* back off! *Don't* retreat! Don't lose courage, yield ground, turn aside, or be deflected. *Don't flinch!*

- Consider starting your meetings with an inspirational passage from the writings or with a brief story from Bahá'í history. Use these brief moments to harmonize your thoughts and to focus on your essential purpose as "trustees of the Merciful."

- Study the writings of Shoghi Effendi. As you work, keep his vision of Bahá'u'lláh's World Order in your thoughts as well as in your deliberations.

- Pray at the start, middle, and end of your meetings. Pray for assistance, guidance, steadfastness, and unity. In short, prayer is your lifeline—*stay connected!*

Suggestions
for Further Reading

General Bahá'í Administrative Guidelines

Local Spiritual Assembly Handbook, 3d ed. Mona Vale, Australia: Bahá'í
    Publications Australia, 1996.

Principles of Bahá'í Administration: A Compilation. London: Bahá'í
    Publishing Trust, 1950.

On Bahá'í Marriage

Bahá'u'lláh. *The Kitáb-i-Aqdas: The Most Holy Book.* 1ˢᵗ pocket-size ed.
    Wilmette, Ill.: Bahá'í Publishing Trust, 1993.

Marriage: A Fortress for Well-Being. Wilmette, Ill.: Bahá'í Publishing
    Trust, 1993.

On Bahá'í Funerals

Death: The Messenger of Joy, comp. Madeline Hellaby. London: Bahá'í
    Publishing Trust, 1980.

*Developing Distinctive Bahá'í Communities: Guidelines for Spiritual
    Assemblies.* Wilmette, Ill.: National Spiritual Assembly of the
    Bahá'ís of the United States, 1989.

On Principles and Tools of Management

Stephen Covey, *First Things First*. New York: Simon and Schuster, 1994.

Bobbi Linkemer, *How to Run a Meeting*. New York: AMACOM, 1987.

Bob Nelson and Peter Economy, *Management for Dummies*. Foster City, Ca.: IDG Books Worldwide, 1996.

Alec Mackenzie, *The Time Trap*. New York: AMACOM, 1990.